WILD ENCHANTRESS

When young Catherine Fulton arrived in Barbados to spend the next few months under the guardianship of Jared Royal, she was no more enthusiastic about the arrangement than he was—and she went out of her way to give him as bad an impression of her as she could. But she couldn't really disguise the fact that he attracted her now just as much as he had all those years ago . . .

WILD ENCHANTRESS

BY

ANNE MATHER

MILLS & BOON LIMITED
17–19 FOLEY STREET
LONDON W1A 1DR

First published 1976
This edition 1977

© Anne Mather 1976

ISBN 0 263 72332 1

*Made and printed in Great Britain by
Richard Clay (The Chaucer Press), Ltd., Bungay, Suffolk*

CHAPTER ONE

ALL he could hear was the rushing, roaring thunder of the water as it splintered on the reef behind him. Ahead lay the beach, creamy white and shimmering in the bleaching rays of the sun, and between, deep green water, alive with the swell that made Flintlock one of the finest surfing beaches on the whole island. Behind him, the crest was rising, foam-flecked and majestic, and his speed increased as he began to coast down the face of the wave. Then it caught him, and his feeling of exhilaration quickened in pace with the surf-board as he rose to his feet and rode diagonally into shore. It was a trial of strength and muscle, keeping erect on that shifting oblong of fibre-glass, controlling its headlong passage with an expertise born of long experience. Before the surf died, he dived off the board into the surging water, and allowed the tow to sweep him on to the warm sand. The surfboard was swept up beside him, shifted restlessly for a few moments, and then was still as he was.

He rolled over on to his back, shading his eyes against the glare of heat which had since childhood given him that deep all-over tan, and felt the familiar feeling of well-being which always followed a successful session. He felt pleasantly relaxed and slightly lethargic, loath to allow the problems of the day to intrude upon these moments of complete self-indulgence.

'Mr Royal! Mr Royal, sir!'

As if to mock his mood of lazy contemplation, Sylvester's throaty voice came harshly on the breeze that stirred the clump of wind-torn cypresses that clung bravely to the

5

coral limestone cliffs that sheltered the cove. Levering himself up on one elbow, Jared Royal looked around and saw the elderly black manservant, incongruous in his chauffeur's livery, beckoning to him from the head of the rocky stairway which gave access to the beach.

With an expression of resigned tolerance on his lean dark features, he got to his feet, and after the briefest use of a towel, he pulled on the shabby denim shorts which were his only clothing. Then, tucking the surfboard under his arm, he trudged up the sand to where a low, bungalow-type dwelling was set on wooden stilts. Sylvester had disappeared, but he would no doubt be sitting in the car ensuring himself of his master's compliance before moving off.

However, Jared was not unduly concerned, mounting the steps to the building with unhurried deliberation. A slat-roofed verandah, overgrown with creeper, gave into the single apartment, a typical beach-house room, with equal space for cooking and sleeping facilities. It was the kind of accommodation used for picnics or weekends, where one could ignore the sand on one's feet and disregard the salt stains on the worn furniture. In one respect it differed from thousands of others like it; the walls were stacked with canvases, one leaning against the other, and easels and painting equipment of all kinds littered what floor space was left. But for all that, Jared liked it, it suited his purpose very well on occasion, and provided an ideal bolthole when his stepmother filled the house with people. He could work here, and he always kept plenty of tinned food on the premises so that he need not be disturbed. If the sleeping facilities were not what he was used to, they at least were adequate.

Now, he dumped the surfboard beside several others in one corner of the room, and crossed to take a can of lager from a gas-cooled refrigerator near the sink. All cooking and lighting appliances were fed by a gas cylinder, but he had had water laid on when the beach house was first built ten years ago.

Standing by the window, looking out on the stretch of sand which tapered away towards the water's edge, he drank deeply from the can, savouring the ice-cold liquid. As he wiped his mouth with the back of his hand, he reflected without enthusiasm on the responsibility ahead of him. Having charge of a young woman already out of her teens seemed an unnecessary encumbrance, and while he appreciated the compliment Jack Fulton had paid him by putting his daughter into his care, he could have wished it were otherwise.

The one occasion he had previously encountered Catherine Fulton had not endeared her to him. At fourteen, she had been a spoilt and precocious adolescent, already aware of her potential, and not above trying her wiles on a man twice her age. Jared had taken an inordinate amount of pleasure in setting her down, and he doubted she had ever forgiven him for that. But her father had been a close friend, and no doubt, without that recurring heart trouble, would never have considered making these emergency arrangements which had come into operation when he died. As it was, Catherine could not touch a penny of the not inconsiderable sum her father had left her until she was twenty-one, which was still some six months away, and Jared had had little choice but to suggest that she came out to Barbados and stayed with him until she gained her inheritance.

He might not have done this—indeed, his inclinations were to allow her to go her own way, except for the letter which Jack had left for him. In it, her father had expressed his own anxieties about the company his daughter was keeping, and his fears that she might marry someone only after her money.

The idea of coming to Barbados had not met with a great deal of approval, he had gathered from her solicitors, via his own. Miss Fulton was apparently enjoying a full and satisfying life in London, and had little desire to spend six months vegetating on an island, Caribbean or otherwise. Besides, she had also let it be known, there was someone, some young man, she preferred not to leave at this time. Royal couldn't help but speculate whether this was the doubtful company her father had been so concerned about.

In the event, he determined that he would not advance her funds to remain in England. He could not possibly maintain any kind of control over her affairs there. So she had had to make the necessary arrangements to leave. That she was due at Seawell this afternoon was a matter of some aversion to him. Remembering the objectionable child she had been, he was not looking forward to his unaccustomed duties as unwilling guardian.

Finishing his lager, he dropped the can into the waste bin and let himself out of the beach house. He didn't lock the door. This beach was private, and besides, apart from the canvases, there was nothing of any value to steal.

He mounted the steps to the cliff top and found Sylvester dozing behind the wheel of a sleek cream Mercedes convertible. But some sixth sense seemed to warn the old man-servant of his approach, and he straightened up as Royal neared the car.

'You can go now, Sylvester,' his employer told him drily. 'I'll follow on.'

'Miz Elizabeth sent me to tell you that it's after eleven, Mr Royal. She says that young lady is arriving at two.'

'Two-thirty, actually,' responded Jared, lightly touching the bonnet of the vehicle and feeling the red-hot heat of the metal send shafts of fire through his fingers. He thrust his hand into the pocket of his shorts and drew out a small case of cheroots. 'Do you have a light?'

Sylvester handed him the automatic lighter from the dash, with unconcealed impatience. 'You don't have time to stand here smoking cigars, Mr Royal,' he exclaimed reprovingly. 'Miz Elizabeth sent me to find you thirty minutes ago!'

His employer ignored him, turning to regard the ocean from the clifftop. It was a magnificent sight and one of which Jared never grew tired. Beyond the reef, the Atlantic surged in all its restless splendour, the creaming line of surf like a bracelet of pearls edging infinity. There was a greeny-blue haze on the horizon and no one could clearly distinguish where the ocean ended and the sky began.

'Well, I'm going now, Mr Royal.'

Sylvester started the Mercedes' engine, and the other man swung round to regard him with a wry smile. 'You do trust me to follow on, then?'

Sylvester sighed. He was not unused to coming down here looking for his employer. He had been doing so for years, since long before old Mr Royal died and his son became the master of the household. It had been a great disappointment to the old man when his only offspring had shown no interest in the business he had built up throughout his lifetime, and preferred painting to any other pursuit. The fact that his son had become extremely successful in his own field had softened the blow a little, but now that the old man was dead, his widow ran the stables quite efficiently with the help of a manager, deferring to her stepson only in the matter of finance.

'I think you should use a car, Mr Royal,' Sylvester said now, shaking his head at the motor-cycle thrown carelessly into the shade of the palms that grew in varying heights beside the track. 'Those things—they're for roughnecks, not for a Royal of Amaryllis!'

His employer hid his amusement, as putting the cheroot between his teeth, he went to haul up the motor-cycle and straddle it comfortably. 'What could be more enjoyable on a day like today than riding through the countryside with the wind cooling your body?'

'You get plenty of wind blowing at you in this here vehicle!' retorted Sylvester. 'What for there's those three limousines up at the house never get used? You wouldn't go to meet that young lady this afternoon on that bicycle, would you?'

Jared Royal grinned, putting up a hand to tug at the thick black hair which was overly long, and which, together with his lack of attire, gave him a piratical appearance. 'Now that's quite an idea, Sylvester——'

'You *wouldn't*!' Sylvester was horrified, and Royal hastened to reassure him.

'No. I guess she might have some objections to her cases hanging over the side,' he mocked, and Sylvester released the Mercedes' brake.

'Your father would turn in his grave if he knew the way you carried on!' he said as his final expression of indignation, and Jared was still smiling as he started the motor-cycle and followed him.

The distance between Flintlock beach and the Royal house was some five miles by road, but on the motor-cycle he could halve that distance by cutting across the paddocks. The horses were used to the noise the motor-bike made, and only the older servants found their master's behaviour a subject for disapproval. But they forgave him, because young and old alike adored the man who since he was a boy had made no distinction between himself and his employees.

He arrived back at the house fully five minutes before

Sylvester, and dumping the motor-cycle near the garages, he walked through the patio area at the back of the house, and in through french windows.

His bare feet made little sound against the tiled floor of the morning room, and he emerged into the hall without encountering anyone. But as he mounted the wide marble staircase to the first floor footsteps sounded in the hall below, and a woman's voice called:

'Jared! Jared, whatever have you been doing? Are you aware it's after twelve o'clock?'

He turned and surveyed his stepmother standing below him. Elizabeth Royal was only two years older than her stepson, and her slender figure and youthful way of styling her hair made her appear younger. In flared coral pants and an emerald green blouse, her curly auburn hair highlighted by the sun glinting through the panes of the window above the main doors to the building, she looked very attractive, and Jared Royal appreciated the fact. With a wry smile, he came down the stairs again, a head taller than she was even with her platform soles.

'You know perfectly well where I've been,' he told her, amusement glinting in his curiously tawny coloured eyes. 'Or did you think I'd been to the Legislature?'

Elizabeth's tongue appeared as she moistened her lips which matched the colour of her pants. 'Darling, you know that girl's arriving in a couple of hours. Don't you think that today at least you could have forgone the disappearing act?'

'No.' Jared thrust his thumbs into the low waistband of his shorts. 'Look, Liz, I don't want you to put yourself out for Catherine Fulton. I wouldn't have had her here at all if it hadn't been for her father's letter. Hell, she's twenty years old! Old enough to make her own mistakes.'

Elizabeth nodded as he was speaking, her fingers linked

11

loosely together, watching him the whole time. Diminutive in stature, she was nevertheless a shrewd businesswoman, and only with Jared did she sometimes adopt an air of helpless femininity.

'You're right, of course, darling,' she murmured. 'But naturally, as mistress of this establishment until you and Laura decide to get married, I don't want to let you down.'

At the mention of his fiancée's name, Jared felt that familiar feeling of impatience. His engagement to Laura Prentiss had in no way been a voluntary one on his behalf, and there were times when he felt as if he was being manoeuvred into a situation from which it would be impossible for him to withdraw. But after his father's death, and the subsequent gossip which had evolved about him and Elizabeth continuing to live at Amaryllis alone together, he had allowed himself to be swayed into announcing a relationship between himself and Laura which until his father's death had been no more than a casual association. Now, almost two years after the event, he was beginning to feel the bands perceptibly tightening. Laura, he knew, wanted to get married, and Elizabeth seemed equally enthusiastic.

With a silent oath, he turned back to the stairs. 'Just leave it all to me, Liz,' he directed, mounting the staircase with easy strides.

When he came downstairs again, Elizabeth was waiting for him in the library, a high-ceilinged room, with book-lined walls and slatted blinds to filter the brilliant sunlight. In cream denim pants, that moulded the contours of his thighs and flared only slightly down the long powerful legs, a cream silk shirt unbuttoned almost to his waist, and drops of water from the shower he had taken still glinting in the darkness of his hair, he looked lean and attractive, and unmistakably male. She came towards him

12

smilingly, holding out a glass of his favourite mixture of rum and Coke, liberally chilled with ice, and he inclined his head in acknowledgement.

'Lunch will be ready in five minutes,' she said, cradling her glass of Martini between her fingers. 'That should give you plenty of time to drive to the airport. What time did you say the flight was due in?'

Jared lowered his glass. 'Two-thirty. Barring accidents.'

'Oh, Jared! You shouldn't say things like that.'

'Why not?' He shrugged. 'All right—God willing, then.'

Elizabeth's lips twitched. 'What God would that be, darling?'

Jared made no reply and moved to stand with his back to the room, staring moodily through the slats in the blind. He was in no mood for idle chatter, and was already bored by the prospect of the wasted afternoon ahead of him.

'Are you sure you wouldn't like me to arrange a dinner party for this evening, Jared?' Elizabeth was speaking again. 'Don't you think it would—well, ease things a little? Laura and her parents would be pleased to come, I know, and Judge Ferris——'

'No!' Jared's harsh denial brought a flush of colour to her cheeks. 'I've told you. There are to be no special parties laid on for Catherine Fulton's benefit.'

'But, Jared, does that mean we've to stop entertaining for the duration of her stay?'

'Of course not.' Jared swung round and swallowed the remainder of the liquid in his glass. 'Just don't overdo it, that's all.' He moved to the drinks trolley and dropped his glass carelessly on to the tray. 'Now—shall we go in to lunch?'

Later that afternoon, driving down the tree-lined road towards the airport, Jared pondered the antagonism he felt towards his dear friend's daughter. Perhaps it was the remembrance that even at fourteen she had had all the instincts of a feline animal, and that now, six years later, she was still attempting to thwart his will with her own. Her choice of the word 'vegetating' to describe the life here in Barbados irritated him immensely, particularly as although he had visited England several times, he had never found London especially appealing. It was too noisy, too dirty, the air was too polluted with petrol and diesel fumes. Obviously, it was the company there she preferred, and Jack expected *him* to play the heavy father now.

He turned the car radio up as if to drown the unpleasantness of that prospect. An American group were playing their latest hit record, a throbbing beat sound that thundered in his ears like the pounding of the surf, and suddenly he relaxed. What was six months after all? One hundred and eighty days. And he could still paint—and swim—and surf! It would soon pass.

An aircraft was droning overhead and he glanced up, wondering whether the flight from Heathrow would land on time. A long and boring journey, he had always found it, usually passing the time by sketching any interesting profile which captured his attention. But sometimes it became embarrassing if he was observed and he had to explain who he was. Publicity, above all things, he abhorred.

Parking the convertible, he vaulted out of his seat, and strolled towards the airport buildings. At this time of the year the airport was invariably busy, with tourists arriving and departing, and the tannoy system working overtime. Somewhere a steel band was playing, its rhythm stirring his blood, and a faintly derisive smile touched the corners of his mouth as he walked slowly into the reception area.

He was not unaware of the several pairs of female eyes which followed his progress. He was not a conceited man,

14

but he had not reached the age of thirty-four without realising his own potential, and for a time he had taken advantage of it. But in recent years he had grown bored with the reputation he had created for himself, and since his engagement to Laura, had avoided any sexual entanglements.

One particular pair of eyes were more persistent than the rest, and he turned to confront their owner with mild impatience. He saw a tall girl with long straight hair streaked in shades of honey and ash blonde. She was slim, but not excessively so, and the tantalising swell of her pointed breasts was visible above the unbuttoned neckline of the striped cotton dress she was wearing. The dress looked like a maternity garment, loose and swinging, its white background striped in shades of violet and purple, the latter exactly matching the colour of her eyes. Her lips parted, as he looked at her, to reveal even white teeth, and there was something familiar about the amusement in her expression. And then he realised why.

Walking towards her, he could feel his whole body stiffening. 'You're—Miss Fulton, aren't you?'

She nodded and smiled, and he wondered how he could have been in any doubt. Six years ago she had been shorter and plumper, the thick hair confined in two bunches, but even then her features had given an indication of what was to come. Now she was quite beautiful, an enchanting picture of burgeoning womanhood. And what else? His eyes probed the length of her slender body, and then returned to her face as she spoke.

'Catherine,' she said easily. 'My name's Catherine. Only you can call me Cat. All my friends do.'

It was seldom that Jared found himself at a loss for words, but this was one of those occasions. Her attitude was so completely unexpected. He had been prepared for anger, and resentment, indifference even. But not this casual amiability.

'I—your plane was early?' he suggested, glancing round for her luggage, and she nodded again.

'I didn't know what to do, and as you had said you would meet me ...'

'Oh, right. Right.' Jared was annoyed at the irritation he felt. 'I'm—sorry I was late.'

'Are you?' Her eyes challenged his, but before he could make some suitable retort, she went on: 'Oh, well, I've only been waiting about five minutes.' She indicated the two suitcases standing behind her. 'These are mine. They're all I've brought. I left the rest of my belongings in the flat. I didn't think there was much point in giving it up, not just for six months.'

Jared regarded her sourly. 'You're very sure you're going back there in six months,' he remarked, and then wondered why he had done so. He didn't want the girl here at all.

'Yes,' she answered now, swinging the strap of a cream leather bag over her shoulder. 'It's my home, after all.'

Jared summoned a porter to take the suitcases, aware of her watching him as he did so. He wondered what she was thinking and was disconcerted when she said: 'It was kind of you to invite me here, but it wasn't necessary. Daddy was always far too protective. I can look after myself.'

'Can you?' Jared's tone was dry. 'Well, I'm sorry, but I felt unable to carry out your father's wishes at several thousand miles' distance.'

'I'm surprised you wanted to,' she murmured, preceding him out into the brilliant sunshine, and again forestalled his retort by adding: 'Gosh, isn't it hot! It was raining when we left London.'

16

The convertible waited in the shade, and Jared had the porter stow her cases in the back, handed him a generous tip, and then swung open the passenger side door for Catherine to get in. He could not help but appreciate the long slender limbs exhibited as she drew her legs into the vehicle, and the perfume she was wearing rose up from the hollow between her breasts. Slamming the door, he walked round and levered himself in beside her, reaching for a cheroot before starting the engine.

'Is it far to your house, Jared?' she inquired, as he inhaled the aromatic fumes deep into his lungs, and he was not pleased by her casual use of his name. When her father had introduced them six years ago, he had been *Mr* Royal, and somehow he had expected that.

'About twenty miles,' he replied shortly, his tone indicative of his mood.

For a few moments there was silence, broken only by the whine of a jet engine overhead, and the sound of laughter across the parking area. Then she said with quiet deliberation: 'Why did you bring me out here, Jared? It's obvious you don't really want me.'

Jared took the cheroot out of his mouth before his teeth crushed it flat. 'Have I given you that impression?'

She looked amused, and that annoyed him even more. 'You know you have,' she said. 'You've never even said *hello*, let alone asked me what kind of a journey I had! What's wrong? Haven't you forgiven me for embarrassing you all those years ago?'

'You didn't embarrass me, Miss Fulton.'

'*Cat*! And yes, I did. I'm sorry. But you were the first man I ever really fell for. I know I was a precocious little beast, but I have grown up a lot since then.'

'It's really not important.'

'So why are you so uptight?'

17

'I'm not—uptight. Whatever that means!'

'You must know. Barbados can't be that out of touch.'

'I don't consider it out of touch at all.'

She gave him a sidelong glance. 'You think I do.'

'Vegetating—isn't that what you said?'

She laughed. 'Oh, no! That got back to you.' She shook her head, 'That was Tony. He said that, not me.'

'Tony?' he queried.

'Mmm. Tony Bainbridge. A—friend.'

'Boy-friend?'

'Well, as he is male ...' She looked amused and Jared ground out the remains of his cheroot in the ashtray.

'The reason why you didn't want to come out here, one presumes,' he commented coldly, and she sighed.

'You do sound pompous,' she said ruefully. 'I didn't think you would be—being an artist and all.'

'I am not an artist!' he retorted grimly. 'I'm a painter. Don't confuse me with your genuine be-smocked eccentric!'

'I wouldn't do that,' she assured him, and he leant forward to start the ignition with a vicious flick of his wrist. She had succeeded in putting hm on the defensive and he didn't like it.

They covered several miles without conversation. She seemed content to stare out of the side of the car at the neat hedges they were passing, at the smooth winding road which might have been in England had it not been for the little wobbling donkey carts with their loads of bananas and grapefruit, mangoes and avocadoes, the dark skins of the people, and cane in the fields instead of corn. Occasionally a white-painted windmill appeared, its sails turning in the breeze which fanned their faces and tangled Catherine's hair. Here and there were cottage gardens bright with flowers of every kind—lilies and begonias,

18

fuchsias, rose mallows, red hibiscus or the exotic petals of the moonflower. It was an exciting and colourful scene, and as the road meandered towards the coast, they came within sight and sound of the Atlantic breakers rolling in to plunging headlands and wild and lovely beaches. The further north they drove, the more spectacular the scenery became and eventually Catherine had to comment upon it.

'It reminds me of Brittany,' she said, leaning forward in her seat to get a better view. 'I had a holiday there when I was about seventeen. Have you ever been to France, Jared?'

He shook his head. 'No.'

She studied his unsmiling profile. 'This—visit isn't going to be much fun if you persist in treating me like some kind of pariah. Look, can't we at least be civil with one another? I know my father would have wanted it that way.'

At the mention of her father, Jared felt a twinge of remorse. Glancing sideways at her, he saw how her eyes had darkened with remembered grief, and he felt a moment's sympathy.

'I liked your father,' he said quietly. 'He was a fine man. I met him in my final year at Oxford. Your mother was alive in those days.'

'Oh, Mummy. Yes.' Catherine sank back in her seat. 'I seem to have been singularly unlucky with my parents. Mummy dying in that car accident, and now Daddy . . .'

Her voice trailed away, and Jared's fingers tightened on the wheel. 'Then it's just as well you can take care of yourself, isn't it?'

His words, not entirely intended to sound ironic, came out that way, and for once she was stung by them. 'That's exactly the kind of remark you would make, isn't it?' she demanded. 'Just because you once got a great deal of satisfaction out of putting me down, you can't resist repeating the experiment, can you?'

'My dear girl——'

'I'm not your dear girl! Oh, how I wish Daddy had never written that letter. I don't know what possessed him to do so. I don't need your guardianship. I was quite happy in London—having a good time——'

'With Tony!' he inserted dryly, and she gave him an angry stare.

'Yes, with Tony. Why not with Tony—or with anyone else, for that matter?'

Jared's expression was contemptuous after this outburst. 'I'm beginning to understand why your father was so concerned about you,' he drawled.

'Oh, are you?' Her eyes challenged his, dark lashes giving them a sooty outline. She examined his face with frank appraisal, and then she said: 'You've got cat's eyes, do you know that? You should have been called Kit, or Christian, so they could have abbreviated your name. With your looks you could easily have been a pirate. What a pity your character doesn't match your appearance!'

'I was not aware you were talking about me. It's obvious. Your father was afraid some man would— would——'

'—put me in the family way? Make me marry him so that he could get his hands on my fortune and I could save my good name? How old-fashioned, Mr Royal,' she taunted. 'Haven't you heard of the pill? And besides, you don't imagine being pregnant would force me to marry anyone, do you?'

Jared's jaw clenched. 'Easy to say, Miss Fulton, when the need doesn't arise!'

Her hands balled together in her lap. 'How do you know?' she demanded scathingly. 'What makes you so sure I'm not pregnant at this moment?'

Jared dragged his eyes away from the road to stare at her, disbelief vying with the recollection of his first sight of her in that loose, flowing garment at the airport. His eyes narrowed, tawny slits between lashes thicker, but not as long, as her own. 'And are you?' he inquired coldly.

Catherine pressed her lips together, deepening colour darkening the soft velvety skin of her cheeks. 'I—yes,' she answered. 'Yes, I am. What are you going to do about it?'

CHAPTER TWO

Now why had she said that?

Catherine could hardly believe she had allowed the words to pass her lips. What possible satisfaction could she hope to gain from such an announcement? How silly to allow him to get under her skin to that extent! It wasn't true. And how angry Tony would be if he ever found out.

And yet she couldn't help but smile at Jared's grim profile as he endeavoured to concentrate his attention on the traffic in the face of her outrageous statement. A small sigh escaped her as she considered how much she had wanted to see him again. Ever since he had come to the Open Day at her boarding school with her father, his image had lingered in her mind, accompanied by that tantalising memory of his reactions to her amateurish attempt to attract his attention.

All the girls had been envious of her attractive visitor. He had worn a denim suit, she remembered, and the closer-fitting styles of those days had accentuated the narrowness of his hips. In any event, she had been pleased to be taking part in the tennis tournament, which meant she had been able to wear a hip-length tennis dress which drew attention to the already curving length of her legs. When her match was over, she had joined her father and his friend for tea, and in the busy marquee it had not been difficult to find an occasion to press herself close to Jared Royal's lean, hard body. That he had swiftly detached himself from her with a few well-chosen words of rebuke had not been able to dispose of the fact that for a brief instant his body had responded to hers. She had not seen him again, but when she learned of her father's letter, she had not been entirely opposed to coming out here and meeting him again. She had thought he might well have forgotten that incident which she remembered so vividly, but it seemed he had not. And what was more, he was judging her present behaviour on one single reckless act. She squared her shoulders. Well, now he had something to justify his opinion of her.

She was so absorbed with her thoughts that she hardly noticed when they turned between griffin-mounted stone gateposts, but the tall palms lining the white-gravelled driveway brought her to the realisation that they were approaching the Royal house. She glanced frustratedly at Jared. Was he not going to say anything, then? Was he so uninterested in her affairs that even the announcement that she was expecting a baby had no reaction on him?

She hunched her shoulders. But what of the rest of his family? What was she going to tell them? She knew he had a stepmother. She could just imagine her reactions to learning her guest's condition. She should never have said what she did. But it was too late now. And besides, she wanted him to believe it. It would give her the greatest pleasure to explode his myth of self-confidence at the end of her stay. And it would also be interesting to see whether he was really as hostile to her as he would have her believe.

But she had to say something, and despising the faint tremor in her voice, she said: 'Is this your home?'

'Yes.' There was a certain amount of pride in his voice now. 'Amaryllis.'

'*Amaryllis.*'

Catherine said the word experimentally. It rolled off her tongue, attractively different from the names of houses

23

back home in England. The drive curved between banks of rhododendrons, and then she saw it. Amaryllis. A wide colonial house, with white-painted shutters, and a long balcony to the first floor, running the width of the house. On the lower floor, rattan chairs were set in the shade between wooden pillars overhung with morning glory and clematis.

'Oh ...' She could not deny the words which tumbled from her lips. 'It's beautiful! So clean—and picturesque. It's like everyone's dream of what a plantation house should be.' She turned to him eagerly, almost forgetting what was between them. 'I expect you love it.'

Jared looked her way, and she was chilled by the coldness of his eyes. Amber should be warm, burnished, not pale and icily penetrating. 'It's my home,' he said expressionlessly.

'But not mine,' she burst out fiercely. 'Is that what you're really saying?'

He shrugged, returning his attention to swinging the convertible round in an arc, bringing it to a halt beside doors which stood wide to the afternoon air. 'I invited you to Amaryllis, Miss Fulton. I haven't forgotten that.'

The car had scarcely stopped before a woman appeared in the open doorway. Catherine, thrusting open her door and getting out of the car without waiting for his assistance, wondered if this could be Jared's stepmother. But as the woman moved further out of the shadows, she saw that she was dark-skinned, and wearing a cotton smock patterned all over with yellow sunflowers on a green background. Her hair was turning grey in places, but was still as thick as ever, and there were laughter creases beside her mouth and eyes. Catherine thought she was going to like her, and judging by the way she was being summed up, the other woman would not forget her face in a hurry.

24

Jared hefted Catherine's cases out of the car and then turned to the woman with a smile which left Catherine wishing he had used his charm on her. 'Lily, this is Miss Fulton who's coming to stay with us for a while. Will you have Henry take her luggage up to her room?'

'Yes, Mr Royal.' Lily's dark eyes shifted to the girl. 'Welcome to Barbados, Miz Fulton.'

'Thank you, Lily.' Catherine cast a slightly ironic glance in Jared's direction. It had taken a servant to say the words he should have used. 'I'm sure I'm going to love it here.' This last, just to show him that he could not intimidate her.

'Where is my stepmother, Lily?'

Not by the flicker of an eyelid did Jared reveal any reaction to his guest's apparent enthusiasm, and Lily led the way into the cool, white-panelled hall of the building, indicating an archway to their right.

'She's in the parlour, Mr Royal. She said to serve tea directly you get back from the airport. Shall I do it now?'

Jared hesitated, while Catherine admired the single crystal chandelier suspended overhead. Then he nodded, adding; 'But bring me a beer, will you, Lily? I need a drink.'

It was his only concession to the tension between them, but Catherine felt unreasonably triumphant as she accompanied him along a cool corridor and into a high-ceilinged sitting room. Her first impressions were of veined marble tiles which reflected the turquoise silk curtains moving gently at the open windows, and deep coral-coloured sofas, bright with cushions in shades of blue, green and turquoise. A woman was reclining on one of the sofas, but at their entrance, she swung her legs to the floor and got to her feet. She was small and slender, elegant in an ankle-length hostess gown made of some chiffon-like material, its burnished autumn shades toning with the reddish lights in her hair. Was this Jared's stepmother? Catherine guessed it was, but she must surely have been years younger than his father.

Jared performed the introductions, calling his stepmother Mrs Royal, and Catherine Miss Fulton. The older woman was weighing her up very thoroughly, and Catherine wondered at that slightly speculative look in her eyes. Then she said, with more warmth than her stepson had shown:

'I think we can dispose of the formalities, don't you, Catherine? That is your name, isn't it? And mine is Elizabeth.'

Catherine couldn't resist darting a glance at Jared's face to see how he was taking this, but he had turned away, ostensibly glancing through several letters laid on a silver salver set on a lacquered cabinet.

'Oh, please do,' she answered now, her nerves tightening a little when she contemplated what this woman's reaction might be if Jared turned round and told her their guest was apparently pregnant. But no, he wouldn't do that. If he did choose to tell his stepmother, it would be at some time when she was not present, when the revelation would not embarrass him.

'Did you have a good journey?'

Elizabeth seated herself on the sofa again and patted the seat beside her, indicating that Catherine should join her. Catherine went to do so, the heat beginning to cause her some discomfort as little trickles of sweat ran down her breasts on to her flat stomach.

'I don't really like flying,' she confessed, aware as she did so that Elizabeth wasn't really paying her a lot of attention. She continually glanced over her shoulder at Jared, and although he continued to ignore them both, Catherine felt the undercurrents in the air. 'Do you?' she finished, and Elizabeth was forced to reply.

'I—why, I don't mind.' She glanced round at Jared

again. 'Darling, did you order tea? I told Lily——'

Jared half turned and looked up. 'Yes.' His gaze flicked to Catherine. 'Perhaps—perhaps our guest might prefer to take tea in her room.'

Catherine put her shoulder bag firmly down on the floor at her feet. 'I'm fine,' she said, aware of his antipathy. 'I'm in no hurry to—wash my hands.' She paused, looking about her. 'What a beautiful house this is.'

'Do you like it?' Elizabeth successfully hid any feelings she had regarding her stepson's behaviour. 'It was built almost a hundred years ago.'

'I adore old houses.' Catherine smiled. 'I live in a very functional flat, and—and when Daddy was alive, I was always trying to persuade him to buy a house.'

'Well, in six months you'll be able to buy one for yourself,' remarked Jared offensively, but she chose to ignore him.

'Have you lived here long, Mrs—er—Elizabeth?'

'Twelve years.' Was there the faintest hesitation before her reply? 'I married Jared's father twelve years ago. Unfortunately, two years ago he died.'

'I'm sorry.'

'Yes.' Elizabeth looked suitably nostalgic for a moment. Then she shook her head. 'Of course, he was a lot older than I am.'

'Of course.'

Catherine caught the inner side of her lower lip between her teeth. There was something about Elizabeth Royal which she didn't altogether like. She didn't know what it was exactly. The woman had been perfectly civil to her. But somehow she felt she preferred Jared's open antagonism to his stepmother's restrained politeness. She was relieved when the squeal of trolley wheels heralded the arrival of tea, but she couldn't suppress the depressing

27

realisation of how long six months could seem.

The tea service was Crown Derby, and between bite-sized sandwiches and several cups of the strong, heavily sweetened beverage she seemed to prefer, Elizabeth kept up a steady inquisition: *Did Catherine live in London? Had she always done so? Did she have her own flat? Had she many boy-friends?*

This latter question was delivered with a coy glance at Jared, who was standing with his back to the open french windows, feet slightly apart, drinking beer from the can despite his stepmother's protests. Catherine was tempted to make some outrageous reply, but a glimpse of his brooding malevolence changed her mind.

'I have—boy-friends,' she conceded slowly. 'I have girl friends, too.'

'But isn't there someone, some particular boy...'

Elizabeth's voice trailed away and she sat regarding her expectantly. Catherine guessed to what she was referring. When news of her father's letter had first reached her, she had made Tony an excuse for wanting to remain in London. And indeed, he had not wanted her to come to Barbados.

Choosing her words carefully, she replied: 'There is one—young man I'm rather friendly with.' She ventured another glance at Jared, but his eyes were fixed on some point above her head. 'His name's Tony Bainbridge. We've known one another for a couple of years.'

'Ah.' Elizabeth seemed relieved, and Catherine wondered about this. Was she worried in case their house-guest began taking too close an interest in her stepson? He was a most attractive—and eligible—man, after all, heir to this estate, however large or small it might be, and a successful portrait painter into the bargain. No doubt all the matrons on the island, with unmarried daughters on their hands, beat a path to his door in an effort to cultivate his attentions, so what was one unmarried female more or less? Certainly nothing for Elizabeth to concern herself about, unless she had some other motive for hoping he remained single ...

At this point Catherine brought herself up short. She had absolutely no grounds for considering any such thing. Whatever his faults, she suspected that Jared Royal was an honourable man, and having an affair with his dead father's widow was hardly an honourable thing to do.

'We must introduce you to Jared's fiancée,' Elizabeth remarked, as if to confound Catherine's speculations, and nullify the intimacy of the look she exchanged with her stepson. 'She's just a little older than you are, but I'm sure you'd find her good company. You could go swimming together, there's a pool out back, or the beach, and we have tennis courts——'

'Perhaps you should let Miss Fulton get used to her new surroundings first,' Jared interposed smoothly, and Catherine realised with a pang that he was actually making things easier for her; or so he thought! A pregnant woman might go easy on the swimming, and avoid tennis altogether.

'Well, I love swimming,' she murmured now, setting her empty teacup on its saucer and waving away Elizabeth's offer of more. 'But I think perhaps Jared's right. I should settle in first.' She looked sideways at him. 'I'm looking forward to meeting your fiancée, though.'

And so she was. She was curious to meet the girl who had succeeded in netting such an unpredictable catch!

Elizabeth appeared to accept this. 'As you wish. Laura—that's Jared's fiancée, by the way—Laura is coming to lunch tomorrow, so you'll meet her then. This evening there'll just be the three of us. Jared thought you might

29

be—tired after your journey.'

Catherine wondered exactly what Jared had thought. What were his motives for bringing her out here? Had it only been a feeling of obligation to her late father which had prompted him to offer her the hospitality of his home? Or might he, like his stepmother, have other reasons?

Stifling a yawn, she realised she was tired. She had been up very early that morning, and the long flight had been singularly boring. The plane had not been full, and the seat beside hers had remained empty, but although she had been superbly comfortable, able to spread her belongings around without fear of disturbing anyone else, she had found it impossible to rest. The magazines offered by the stewardesses had failed to distract her thoughts from the anticipation of her arrival, and she had been impatient to reach her destination. But now she was here, she knew what she was up against, and within half an hour of her arrival she had placed herself in an entirely false position.

Elizabeth had apparently noticed her efforts to hide her weariness, for she gave a sympathetic smile before getting to her feet and ringing a bell on the wall by the door. A young maid appeared, and her mistress gave her instructions to show Miss Fulton to her room.

'I'm sure you'll find everything you need, Catherine,' she said, as her guest stood up and walked towards the door. 'If not, Susie'—she indicated the maid—'will attend to it. We have dinner at about eight o'clock. I should rest for a while, if I were you.'

'Thank you.' Catherine turned to look at both of them. Well, now Jared would have an opportunity of apprising his stepmother of the situation, or at least, what he thought was the situation. She half wished she had not been so impulsive. 'I—thank you for inviting me here,' she added. 'I'm sure I'm going to—enjoy myself.'

30

Jared half turned to stare out of the window, and Catherine felt her hackles rise. He was so arrogant! Why should she regret anything she had said to him? It was left to his stepmother to assure her that she was very welcome, and then Susie led the way back to the hall.

A marble staircase led to a first floor gallery which circled the hall below. White panelled doors opened on to the gallery, but Susie turned left at the top of the stairs into a long panelled hallway giving access to that wing of the building. She flung open a heavy door halfway along the hall, and indicated that Catherine should precede her into the room.

She stepped into an apartment fragrant with the perfume from a bowl of roses set on the bedside table. White damask-covered walls were relieved by the long rose-coloured curtains at the open balcony doors, and echoed in the silken bedspread strewn with red roses on a white background. The cedarwood furniture was light and functional, adding its own distinctive aroma to the already heady scent of the room.

Susie crossed the fluffy white rugs which were strewn over the wood-blocked floor to open the adjoining bathroom door, but Catherine had already stepped on to the balcony, catching her breath at the view which confronted her. There in the distance was the sea, hazed in green and blue, shimmering through the heat of late afternoon. Between the house and the ocean stretched acres of pastureland, grazed by groups of horses, their coats dark splashes against the greenness of the grass. Immediately below her windows were the gardens of the house. Formal lawns and flower beds, tennis courts half hidden behind hedges of laurel and rhododendron, and opening from the house itself, a mosaic-tiled patio area, bright with garden furniture, and reflected in the depths of an enormous kidney-shaped swimming pool. Its blue waters looked cool and inviting, and had Catherine not felt so utterly weary, she might well have taken advantage of that particular amenity before dinner.

'Can I get you anything else, Miss Fulton?'

Susie was hovering right behind her, and Catherine came back into the bedroom, looking about her with smiling appreciation.

'I don't think so, thank you. It's beautiful.'

The maid smiled her satisfaction at these words and gave a little bob. Then she noticed the cases set on an ottoman at the foot of the bed. 'Would you like me to unpack for you?' she suggested, but Catherine shook her head, assuring her that she could manage. 'Well, the bell's just there, by the door,' Susie added, her voice soft and slightly sing-song. 'If you do need any help, just ring.'

When she was alone, Catherine breathed a sigh of relief and leaned back against the door to survey her domain. It was all far more luxurious than she had expected. Her father had talked very little about Jared's background, confining his remarks to the man's undoubted artistic ability, and the fight he had had with his father to leave Oxford and attend an art college. Her father had been lecturing at that time, before he gave it up to concentrate his energies towards a political career. But now she was left in no doubt as to her host's affluence, and she wondered if this was the main reason why her father had chosen such a guardian for her. Perhaps it was yet another attempt to persuade her of the foolishness of her own intentions.

The bathroom which adjoined the bedroom had porcelain tiles, patterned with the continuing rose design. Long mirrors gave back her reflection from a dozen different angles, and cut glass shelves supported a variety of oils and lotions intended to add their fragrance to the water.

Catherine decided to have a bath, shedding her clothes carelessly, too tired to fold them, or unpack her cases right now. Cool water melted the heat from her body and left her feeling infinitely refreshed. Wrapping herself in a white towelling bathrobe which she found hanging behind the bathroom door, she came back into the bedroom and stretched her length on the superbly comfortable springs of the bed, uncaring that her hair was damp and strewn carelessly across the pillows, or that her bare feet made little wet patches on the immaculate bedspread.

CHAPTER THREE

SHE awoke to the sound of birds arguing in the trees that cast pools of shade around the patio area. At first it was difficult to feel any sense of identity with her surroundings, but then it all came flooding back to her—her father's death six weeks ago, the summons and subsequent flight to Barbados, and the strange welcome which had been awaiting her.

She blinked, realising she was no longer lying on the bed, but in it, silk sheets caressing her bare legs. Her hands groped for the bathrobe. She was still wearing it, but the cord had become unloosened and the lapels had parted.

That daylight was coming through the slats of the blinds which had been drawn confused her, and she reached automatically for her watch which she always left on a table beside her bed. As she did so, something registered. There had been roses beside the bed before she went to sleep. Now they were gone.

The hands of her watch mocked her. Six-fifteen! Had she slept for barely an hour? It was impossible. She felt completely rested. Unless . . .

She pushed back the covers and swung her feet to the floor, finding the rug soft to her toes. The balcony doors had been closed by whoever had drawn the blinds and taken away the roses, but a window had been left ajar. Catherine unfastened the doors now and thrust them open, wrapping her robe closer about her as she stepped outside.

Her suspicions had been correct. Even without the golden orb of the sun spreading its brilliance over a sky translucently washed in pinks and lemon and turquoise, the coolness of the air compared to the softness of the evening before would have convinced her. A faint mist still hovered low over the meadow, and the scent of the ocean came strongly before the awakening blossoms in the garden overlaid the air with their perfume. There was no sound to be heard in the house, and she felt assured that no one would observe her standing here at this early hour. The balcony, which was a continuation of the one which ran across the front of the house, was separated from the rooms on either side by a vine-hung trellis, but that would prove no screen to prying eyes.

Fastening the cord of the bathrobe more tightly, she stretched her arms luxuriously above her head. She must have slept for twelve hours, and now she felt thoroughly wide awake and restless. The pool looked as inviting now as it had done the evening before, but somehow she was loath to use it and possibly arouse the other members of the household. The ocean beckoned, and she wondered whether it was possible to reach it across the paddocks. Even from this distance, she could see the line of foam where it surged over the reef, and her skin tingled at the prospect of plunging into its depths.

Turning back into the bedroom, she opened her suitcases and stared thoughtfully at their contents. The clothes she had discarded so untidily the night before had disappeared, and she guessed that whoever had drawn the covers over her and attended to the shutters, had taken them away for laundering. It was a curious sensation thinking she had been so soundly asleep that not even a servant's hands had awakened her.

She rummaged through the contents of one of the cases and brought out a pair of purple denim jeans and a spotted cotton smock with wide, elbow-length sleeves and a tie belt. The strap of a white bikini emerged from the disorder, and on impulse, she pulled the bikini out as well.

In her bathroom, she took a quick shower, taking care not to wet her hair, and then dressed, first in the bikini, and then in the jeans and smock. A brush brought a silky sheen to her thick straight hair, and she looped it back behind her ears but otherwise left it loose.

Her room door made no sound as she opened it, and she made her way along the hall and across the gallery to the stairs. Marble did not creak under her sandal-clad feet, but when she reached the hall the heavy doors were securely closed. Frowning, she turned through the archway leading to the room where she had taken tea with Elizabeth Royal, and finding that door went inside. French doors were easier to unfasten, and with impatient fingers she slid back the bolts and stepped outside.

She was at the side of the building where green leaves gave on to a trellised rose arbour, but she followed the line of the house around to the back and came upon the patio. The air was like wine, slightly sharp and invigorating, and she moved her shoulders in a gesture of complete indulgence of the senses.

Then, out of the corner of her eye, she glimpsed a tall figure, moving beyond the bushes near the tennis courts. It was Jared, and hardly stopping to consider what she intended to do, Catherine ran around the swimming pool, pushed her way between laurel bushes and emerged on to a crazily-paved path. Jared was some way ahead now, astride a motor-cycle, she saw in surprise, but obviously waiting until he was out of sound of the house before starting the engine.

'Hey!' she called, running down the path after him. 'Jared! Wait!'

Her voice came clearly on the still morning air, and

36

he halted at once and swung round to stare at her. Not very amicably, she saw, as she came closer. Like her, he was wearing jeans, but nothing else, his skin smooth, and only lightly covered with hair.

'Hello,' she said determinedly. 'Where are you going?'

Jared swung his leg over the motor-bike, stood it on its rest, and faced her squarely. 'I might ask you the same question.'

Catherine refused to be put off. 'I'm sorry I didn't make dinner last evening. I must have been more tired than I thought. But it was such a beautiful morning, I couldn't bear to stay in my room a moment longer.'

Jared acknowledged this small speech with a faint inclination of his head. 'You must be hungry,' he said. 'Lily's probably about by this time. If you go into the parlour and ring the bell, she'll get you anything you want.'

Catherine pursed her lips. 'I'm not hungry! At least, not especially so. I don't feel like eating at this moment. I feel like swimming!'

Jared shrugged his broad shoulders. 'Feel free to use the pool any time you like.'

Catherine controlled her temper with difficulty. 'But I don't want to use the pool either,' she said, through her teeth. 'I want to swim in the sea. It's warm, isn't it? I've never swum in the Caribbean before.'

Jared cast a lazy glance towards the ocean. 'That's the Atlantic, actually,' he drawled, and she glowered at him.

'You know what I mean!'

Jared regarded her without emotion. 'Ought you to—well, swim at all in your—condition?'

Catherine expelled her breath on a sigh. 'Of course. Lots of women swim until they're seven or eight months. And—and I'm still measuring my pregnancy in weeks, not months!'

Jared's expression darkened. 'Then I suggest you have Sylvester—he's the chauffeur—take you down to the beach later on this morning.'

Catherine looked up at him frustratedly. 'You still haven't told me where you're going.'

'No, I haven't.'

'I want to come, too.'

'What?' For once she seemed to have succeeded in getting under his skin. 'Miss Fulton, I don't know what kind of society you've been mixing in in England, but out here a girl waits to be invited before encumbering some man with her company!'

'Really?' Catherine managed to sound bored. 'Well, you invited me out to Barbados, *Mr* Royal, and I think it's up to you to entertain me! Hmm?'

Jared looked furious, and just in case he suddenly decided to fling himself on to the motor-bike and ride off, Catherine swung her leg across the machine and perched herself precariously on the back.

'Get off that bike!' Jared glared at her, but she just put on her sweetest smile. 'You're not about to tell me that pregnant women do that until they're seven or eight months!'

'No,' Catherine conceded, flicking a butterfly with exotic crimson and black colouring away from her face, 'but it won't do me any harm—providing you take it easy.'

Jared moved his head slowly from side to side. 'Do you want me to drag you off?'

'Oh, would you do that?' she exclaimed disbelievingly. 'To an expectant mother?'

Jared looked angrier than ever, but he made no attempt to shift her, and Catherine realised she was enjoying this. It was stimulating and exciting, provoking him like this, but perhaps not entirely fair. Feeling a need to justify herself, she said appealingly:

'Please, Jared! Don't be mean. Let me come with you.'

'You can't.'

'Why not?'

'Because I'm going to the beach——'

'I knew you were!' she exclaimed triumphantly.

'—across the fields!'

Catherine frowned. 'I don't understand.'

'Look, it's five miles round by road. It's less than half that distance across the paddock.'

'I see.' Catherine drew her lower lip between her teeth. The idea of riding across the bumpy turf on the motorbike sounded like fun, but it was something she could not undertake without exploding the myth of her phoney pregnancy.

'So—will you get off the bike?'

Jared looked grim, but she wouldn't give in that easily. 'Couldn't we—couldn't you take the road for once?' she suggested hopefully.

'No, I——' Jared broke off to regard her dourly for a moment. Then he gave a heavy sigh. 'All right, Miss Fulton, you win. I'll take you to the beach—but in the convertible.'

'Oh, no!' Catherine had been looking forward to riding on a motor-bike again. She had had one once, when she was sixteen.

'Oh, yes. Come on.' He was impatient now, holding out a hand to assist her to dismount, which she took with ill grace. 'Don't be surprised if you haven't woken up the whole household.'

But she hadn't, and when they drove away from the garages, only old Sylvester saw them leave. It was marvellous, feeling the cool air in their faces, and Catherine found she was actually looking forward to this hour alone with her reluctant escort.

Jared parked the car on a headland overlooking a wild and beautiful stretch of beach, the sand bleached white by the sun, where the surf came thundering in from the reef. But when she would have got out of the car, he stopped her, saying: 'You can't swim here. This is Flintlock. I come surfing here.'

'Is this where you were headed this morning?'

He nodded, and would have started the engine again, only she stopped him, her slim fingers curving round his wrist. 'Don't,' she said, withdrawing her hand when he turned to look at her. 'I've done some surfing. Not a lot, but some—in Cornwall. That's the southernmost corner of England.'

'I know where Cornwall is,' he said dryly.

'Oh! Oh, well, then. Why can't we try it now? I'm willing.'

Jared's eyes dropped pointedly to her stomach. 'Are you?'

'Yes, of course.' She sighed, colouring in spite of herself. 'I've told you, it's months and months away. I don't intend doing anything reckless. But I don't want to spoil your—your pleasure.'

'Haven't you done that already?' he countered, and she glared at him.

'Well? Have I?'

His eyes probed hers for a long disturbing moment, and then he thrust open his door and climbed out. 'I'll let you know,' he replied enigmatically.

There were steps down to the beach, and Jared went ahead, glancing round from time to time to assure himself that she was all right. Catherine couldn't help feeling touched by this involuntary display of concern on her behalf, although she guessed he would have done the same for anybody.

Halfway down, they came in sight of a low beach house, set in the lee of the cliffs and not visible from above. It stood on supports, a couple of feet above the sand, and as they came down the last of the steps Jared said: 'This is mine. I work here sometimes. And it's useful as a retreat!' this last with a meaning glance in her direction.

Catherine tossed back her hair, and walked across the sand, kicking off her sandals and carrying them. She climbed the shallow steps to the shaded verandah and looked in through the sand-dusted windows.

Jared seemed to hesitate, and then he said: 'The door isn't locked. You can go in, if you want to.'

Catherine looked round at him, could read no hidden menace in his expression, and turned the handle of the door. Inside, there was a faint smell of oil pants and canvas, and looking round the room she could see why. There was a stove in one corner, for heating on cooler days, she presumed, a couple of squashy leather chairs which were worn in places, a low table, cupboards for storing things, and a cooker, sink and refrigerator. But in every available space there were stacks of canvases, strewn haphazardly around the walls, and propped against an easel which leaned drunkenly against one of the chairs.

She stood just inside the door looking about her, and Jared came to support himself against the jamb, regarding her without evident hostility for once. 'Well?' he said, making it a question. 'Are you appalled at the mess?'

Catherine half turned towards him. 'Why should I be? I expect you work very well here.'

He frowned. 'Why do you say that?'

'I don't know.' She shrugged her slim shoulders. 'It's the disorder, I suppose. I read something once, I don't remember where—in one of those trendy journals, I think

41

—and it said something about order being without inspiration. That creating anything—artistic, in disciplined surroundings, is like mining for diamonds in a velvet-lined box.'

Jared straightened, his lips twisting mockingly. 'How very apt! And how perceptive of you to remember it.'

Catherine sighed. 'Sometimes those articles are just rubbish! I just thought that particular one had some merit.'

'Oh, it did.' Jared passed her and walked indolently across the room, kicking aside a tube of paint which oozed stickily on to the bare boards. He indicated a divan in one corner, half hidden from her view by other paraphernalia. 'I sleep here sometimes. It's quiet, and I don't mind the sound of the ocean. And, as you say, I enjoy the chaos.'

He looked at her as he spoke, and she felt a curious warning sensation in the pit of her stomach. When he was not using the sharp edge of his sarcasm against her, he was disturbingly attractive, and the girlish feelings he had aroused all those years ago did not seem quite so distant after all.

As though realising that for a few moments he had forgotten his antipathy towards her, he withdrew his gaze from hers and hauled a couple of surfboards out from behind the door. One was bigger than the other, but they were both made of fibre-glass and very light.

'Are you sure you want to try this?' he asked, his voice hard and slightly impatient, and she nodded eagerly.

'Of course. Is this one mine?' She indicated the smaller board. 'Hmm, smell that scent of the sea!'

They came down the steps on to the beach and looked towards the ocean. The sun glittered and danced on the water, dazzling the eyes, jewelling the foam to sparkling brilliance. The sun was rising higher, and its heat was making the sand warm beneath their feet.

Catherine bent her head to unzip her jeans and Jared gave her an angry look. 'What are you doing?'

She looked up in surprise. 'I don't normally go swimming in my jeans,' she answered innocently.

He expelled his breath noisily. 'You can change in the beach house.'

'I don't have to change.' She wriggled the jeans down over her hips, revealing the narrow band of the bikini. 'I came prepared.' She smiled. 'Didn't you?'

Jared said a word which she wouldn't have liked to repeat, and unfastened his own jeans and slid them down his legs. His swimming trunks were black and came beautifully low on his lean hips. Catherine couldn't help admiring the powerful muscles so displayed, but he obviously disliked her eyes upon him. Picking up a surfboard, he strode away down the beach, and she stood there folding her jeans and watching him.

He carried the surfboard into the waves until the water was up to his waist, then he straddled the board before stretching his length upon it, paddling out towards the line of the reef with steady progression.

Catherine was hardly aware that she had bent and picked up the untidy pile that was his jeans, or that as he approached the turning point, she pressed them closely to her chest, watching for the surf to catch him with such intensity that her eyes ached from the glare.

He had turned. He was kneeling on the board now, coasting down the inside of the crest which threatened to engulf him. Her heart leapt into her throat as the board was lifted high on the swell, and then he was on his feet, balancing himself with an expertise she couldn't help but envy, driving diagonally in towards the shoreline at what seemed an incredible speed. If he should lose his balance, if he should fall . . .

She closed her eyes and when she opened them again, he had disappeared. She took several involuntary steps forward, her heart hammering so loudly it seemed audible. Then she saw the surfboard tossed carelessly by the waves, and her heart seemed to stop beating altogether. She ran towards the water's edge, blinking as shafts of green brilliance obscured her vision. The sun was reacting on her unguarded eyes, making them water just when she wanted to see clearly.

She moved her head from side to side, searching for a glimpse of him, and then gulping with relief when he appeared some distance to her left, thrown upon the sand like the surfboard beside him. She ran eagerly towards him, still clutching his jeans, but he was getting to his feet and his expression was not encouraging.

'What the hell are you doing?' he demanded, and she blinked at him bewilderingly. 'What's the matter? Why are you looking at me like that? And what are you doing with my pants?'

He tugged the offending jeans out of her grasp, and she stood there before him, still wearing her smock, still too shocked to say much at all.

'I—I—you disappeared. I thought—I thought——'

'You thought I'd drowned?'

'Well, I—I wasn't sure . . .'

Jared tossed his jeans on to the sand, and Catherine noticed inconsequently that they had landed in the same heap as before. 'I dived off the board, before it reached shallow water,' he told her impatiently. 'I'm sorry if you were alarmed, but I didn't know you were watching me.'

Catherine was gradually recovering her composure, and resentment gave her a welcome barrier against the feelings she had just experienced. 'I'm sure you knew perfectly well that I was watching you,' she retorted, aware as she

44

did so that she was not sure of any such thing.

Jared sighed. 'Why? Why aren't you in the water yourself?'

'I'm no expert. You must know you are.'

'Thank you.' His tone was sardonic. 'So why were you so concerned?'

She stared up at him angrily. Without the platform soles she was used to, he was several inches taller than she was, a new experience for her because she was a tall girl. 'I really don't know!' she told him feelingly, and marched away along the beach.

Her desire to swim had left her. Her eyes still ached from the glare of the water, and an awful empty feeling was making itself felt in the region below her rib-cage. After all, she had not eaten since yesterday afternoon, and then only two of the diminutive sandwiches. She sat down on the sand beside the other surfboard, drawing up her legs and wrapping her arms around them, resting her chin on her knees.

She was hardly aware of him coming to join her, until his weight disturbed the sand beside her, and she permitted herself the knowledge that he was standing beside her.

'I'm sorry if you were upset,' he said quietly, and ridiculously, his apology moved her to tears.

'It doesn't matter,' she mumbled into her knees, but he must have discerned the break in her voice, and he uttered an expletive before coming down on his haunches beside her.

He remained there silently for several seconds just looking at her, and eventually she felt compelled to look at him. He was very close, his skin still damp with sea water, smelling slightly of the salt. There was hair on his arms and legs, fine dark hair, the ends bleached golden by the sun. She knew the strongest impulse to put out her hand and stroke the taut muscles of his thigh, to feel that smooth brown skin beneath her fingers. She didn't seem capable of lifting her eyes, and with another exclamation he got to his feet.

'Do you want to swim?' he demanded roughly, and she dug her chin into her knees before replying.

Then, brushing a careless hand across her cheeks, she got to her feet, shaking her head. 'No.' She bent to pick up her jeans. 'But don't let me stop you.'

'No, I won't do that,' he muttered bitterly, and without another word began to pull his pants on over his wet trunks.

Catherine bit her lip. 'Oughtn't you to take those off?' she asked, and his eyes bored coldly into hers.

'I suppose you'd like to help me!' he remarked harshly, and although her colour deepened, she didn't flinch from the challenge.

'If you'd like me to,' she countered steadily, and he uttered a sound of disgust.

'It would be no novelty to you, I suppose!'

'It never was—a novelty, I mean,' she murmured, and then concluded by despising herself as he strode angrily away.

It was, amazingly, barely nine o'clock when they arrived back at the house. Jared parked the car on the sweep of drive before the now open front doors, and leaving Catherine to fend for herself, walked grimly indoors. But when she followed him a few moments later, she found he had encountered his stepmother in the hall, and she was gently reproving him for disappearing so early in the day. This morning Elizabeth Royal was dressed in a cream silk shirt and well-cut riding breeches, narrow black boots completing a picture of diminutive elegance. Jared had apparently not yet told her that he had not been alone, and when Catherine appeared, Elizabeth's eyes widened in arrant disbelief.

46

Catherine found herself waiting for the inevitable comment about her condition, but it didn't come. Instead, Elizabeth ignored her, turning to her stepson and saying:

'I don't understand, Jared. I thought you had been to to the beach.'

'I have.' Jared's eyes had the coldness of marble in their depths when they encountered Catherine's. 'She—Miss Fulton, that is—came with me.'

It seemed ridiculous that he should go on calling her *Miss* Fulton when their exchanges were so much less than polite. Elizabeth seemed to think nothing of it, and yet she had addressed their guest as Catherine. But then perhaps she preferred that they remain formal with one another, thought Catherine, with a return of her cynicism of the afternoon before.

Now Elizabeth was forced to acknowledge the girl's presence, and again Catherine waited for the expected denunciation. But Elizabeth merely gave her the faintest of smiles, and said rather stiffly: 'How fortunate you were not to get your hair wet.' She looked at her stepson and stretched up her hand to touch the virile darkness of his. 'Yours is soaking, darling.'

Catherine found her nails were digging rather painfully into her palms. 'I—I didn't swim, Mrs Royal.' Impossible to call her Elizabeth at this moment. 'I just—watched Jared.'

Jared turned away to the stairs. 'Excuse me.'

'What about your breakfast?' His stepmother's voice followed him plaintively.

Jared paused and looked down. 'I'll get something later. Have Susie make me some coffee. I'm not particularly hungry.'

Elizabeth's lips tightened as he disappeared through a door off the gallery, and it was with an obvious effort that

47

she forced herself to be civil to their guest.

'Are you hungry, Catherine? Of course, you must be.' Catherine stiffened, and then relaxed once more as her hostess went on: 'You didn't have any dinner last evening.'

Following Elizabeth across the hall, and into a small, sunlit morning room, where a circular table was laid with a white cloth, Catherine apologised. 'I must have been tireder than I imagined. I had a bath, and I don't remember much after that.'

Elizabeth's smile was a shade easier. 'No. Well, never mind. It's always best to get over jet lag at the earliest opportunity. And we quite understood. Jared sent one of the servants to make sure you were all right.'

'You're very kind.' *But what else had Jared told her?*

'Not at all. We want you to feel that this is your home —for the next six months anyway.' Catherine had to smile at the way this was hastily tacked on, limiting their generosity. 'We—Jared and I, that is—want you to relax here.'

Catherine wasn't quite sure that she liked the coupling of their names. While it was physically obvious that Elizabeth could not be a lot older than her stepson, culturally speaking they should be poles apart. Elizabeth had been married for twelve years to a man at least twenty years her senior, while Jared had never experienced the total commitment of such a relationship. And yet Elizabeth spoke as if they were equals, sharing a common interest.

Susie appeared, and Elizabeth told Catherine to order whatever she liked. She had already eaten, she said, but she joined her guest for coffee, and remained with her while she ate fresh fruit and cereal, rolls and apricot conserve. Catherine would have preferred to be alone. She needed time to assimilate her position here. But Elizabeth had evidently decided to apprise her of the normal running of the household.

'We breed racehorses,' she said. 'Did Jared mention it to you?' Catherine shook her head. 'We have quite a successful record.' She waved a careless hand towards the windows. 'You must have seen the horses in the paddock.'

Catherine put a slice of honey-sweet peach into her mouth and nodded, wiping her sticky fingers on her table napkin. 'I did see the horses, yes. But I didn't realise ...' She shrugged. 'I thought Jared—painted.'

Elizabeth gave a light, patronising laugh. 'Oh, my dear, he does. And very successfully, too. But the horses—they were his father's pride and joy.'

'I see.'

'When James—that was Jared's father's name'—Catherine noticed she did not say *my husband*, 'when James died, I took over the stables. We have a very efficient manager, an Irishman by the name of Patrick Donovan, and I like to think that we've continued to maintain the high standard Royal horses have always been noted for.'

Catherine smiled. There was little she could say which would not sound like a cliché. She liked horses. She had ridden frequently when she was a child. But it was some years now since she had mounted any animal ... unless you could count a camel on a visit with her father to Saudi Arabia!

'Do you ride, Catherine?'

It was a reasonable question, but Catherine realised it had other implications. Was it the kind of question Elizabeth would ask a girl she thought to be pregnant? Or was it perhaps a catch question, intended to draw from her guest the information she had thrown so carelessly at her stepson?

Deciding there was no point in burning her bridges until she had crossed them, Catherine chose the easy way out. 'I have done,' she conceded. 'But not for years.'

'Then we must find you a mount,' exclaimed Elizabeth, pouring herself more coffee. 'It's the only way to explore the island. We must find you an escort, too. I'm giving a little dinner party tomorrow evening, and I shall invite one or two young men I know who will be enchanted to meet you.'

'Really, that's not necessary.' Catherine made a deprecatory gesture. 'You don't have to entertain me, Mrs Royal.'

'Elizabeth. And I know that, my dear. But—well, I hope you won't take this amiss, but I don't want you making a'—the word *nuisance* hovered on the tip of her tongue, Catherine could almost see it!—'making things—difficult for Jared.' She hastened on before her guest could intervene. 'This morning, for instance. Jared goes down to the beach most mornings. It's his—sabbatical time, do you know what I mean? The time when he—when he thinks'— she spread her hands extravagantly—'when he—recharges his batteries, as it were. His work is *so* demanding. You must appreciate that. He needs time to be alone. No one ever intrudes!'

'I'm sorry.' There didn't seem much else to say. And she could hardly deny being aware of his extreme reluctance to take her!

'I'm sure you meant no harm, my dear.' Elizabeth could afford to be generous now her point had been well and truly made. 'But you'll learn that in this household, we all make allowances for the—how shall I put it?—artistic temperament?'

Catherine finished her breakfast without enjoyment, but Elizabeth, having delivered her little speech, began to excuse herself to go about her own duties.

'You do whatever you like, my dear,' she said, getting

to her feet and brushing a speck of dust from the immaculately fitting jodhpurs. 'Sunbathe, if you like, or have a swim in the pool. The house is yours. Jared will probably spend the rest of the morning in his studio, but Laura should be here by twelve. I would show you the stables, but I have to go over the accounts with Donovan this morning, and we have a prospective buyer coming at eleven.'

'That's all right.' Catherine pushed back her chair. 'Don't bother about me, I can look after myself.'

'I'm sure you can.' Was there a trace of irritation in the smooth, cultured tones? 'Well, I'll see you later, then.'

'Thank you.'

Catherine didn't quite know what she was thanking her for, but she breathed a sigh of relief when Elizabeth left her, realising her gratitude could well be attributed to this awaited release. It was obvious that for some reason Elizabeth felt the need to specify the situation here in no uncertain terms, leaving Catherine in no doubt as to her insignificance in the general scheme of things.

CHAPTER FOUR

THE morning passed reasonably quickly. Catherine collected her dark glasses from her room, and settled on one of the comfortable loungers beside the pool, removing her jeans and smock, and smoothing oil into her pale skin. Although she was fair, she usually tanned easily, and she hoped it wouldn't be long before her skin lost that sun-starved appearance, a reminder of winter in England. Stretched on the lounger, with the sun pouring its rays down upon her, it was easy to give herself up to a welcome feeling of well-being, much different from the veiled antagonism evident in so much of what Elizabeth had had to say. At eleven o'clock, Susie brought out a tray on which reposed a jug, clinking with iced orange juice, and the sharp, tangy flavour was coolly refreshing. The maid also suggested that it wasn't wise to spend too long in the full glare of the sun on her first day, and Catherine did not object when she moved a large multi-coloured striped umbrella so that its fringed canopy provided a barrier to her already burnished arms and legs.

She had pushed her dark glasses up above her forehead, and was slowly savouring another glass of fruit juice when the clatter of heels across the mosaic tiling caused her to glance round. A girl was coming towards her, taller than Elizabeth but not so tall as herself, with shoulder-length dark hair which curved confidingly into the nape of her neck, and serene, even features. She was wearing a halter-necked sundress, patterned in shades of yellow and blue, that made the most of smooth tanned arms. Catherine guessed at once that this was Laura, Jared's fiancée, and she swung her legs to the ground and reached for the smock she had discarded earlier.

'Please—don't get up.' Laura's voice was warm and friendly. 'You look so comfortable! You must be Catherine, of course. And I'm Laura, Laura Prentiss. How do you do?'

Catherine pulled her long hair free of the neckline of the smock, and held out her hand in response to Laura's. 'Yes, I'm Catherine Fulton. Hello.'

Laura subsided on to an adjacent lounger, pulling her skirt down over her knees, and making Catherine wish she had had time to put on her jeans as well. 'Welcome to Barbados. Do you think you're going to like it here?'

'Oh, I'm sure I shall.' Catherine made a gesture which encompassed the pool and gardens and the countryside beyond. 'Who wouldn't?'

Laura nodded. 'I'm biased, I'm afraid. I've always lived here, and I always want to do so. Once an islander, always an islander.'

Catherine was tempted to point out that the British were islanders, too, but she thought it might sound rather rude, so she just smiled and waited for Laura to continue.

'I was sorry to hear about your father,' she added disarmingly, and Catherine felt she really was.

'Are your parents living on the island, Laura?' she asked, after acknowledging her condolences.

'Heavens, yes.' Laura smiled. 'You can't get Mummy to go away, not even for a holiday. As she says, what could we possibly find elsewhere that we haven't already got here?'

Catherine could think of any number of things, but she bit her tongue. Their attitude was insular in the extreme, but then they would probably be the first to acknowledge

53

this and be proud of it.

'And have you travelled, Laura?' she asked politely, half wishing that Elizabeth would appear so that she could make her escape and go and change.

'Well, I went to the United States with Daddy once,' replied Laura thoughtfully. 'And I've visited some of the other islands. But that's all. I went to school in Bridgetown. I don't suppose you've been there yet.'

'No. I only arrived yesterday afternoon, and I was so exhausted, I'm afraid I slept all evening and night as well.'

Laura nodded sympathetically. 'I'm not surprised. It's a long journey. I'd never make such a journey on my own.'

'Oh?' Catherine raised her dark eyebrows. 'Why not?'

Laura's laugh was girlish. 'I'd be terrified! All that way without anyone to talk to, not knowing what one was going to meet at the end of it!'

Catherine realised that there were women who felt like this, and tempered her impatience with humour. 'That's no way to speak of your fiancé,' she remarked dryly, but Laura didn't notice the irony.

'I suppose once Jared and I are married, I'll have to get used to travelling,' she mused. 'He's often invited to lecture in North America, and occasionally he goes to England. But then you know that, don't you? That was how he met your father.'

Catherine heard more footsteps, but they proved only to be Susie's again, come to see whether Miz Prentiss might like some coffee.

'Miz Royal says she'll be joining you directly,' she added, which was more to Catherine's liking, 'and Mr Royal—oh, he's coming right now!' which was not.

Laura got eagerly to her feet as Jared appeared, strolling across the patio towards them. In close-fitting gaberdine pants, and a navy blue silk shirt, unbuttoned at the neck and the cuffs turned back, he looked coolly masculine, a gild signet ring, his only piece of jewellery, glinting on his little finger. His gaze barely touched Catherine, but she registered the contempt in his eyes, before his expression warmed to greet his fiancée.

They kissed. Watching them, Catherine acknowledged a certain satisfaction in the awareness that their embrace was anything but passionate. Laura's lips never parted when they encountered her fiancé's, and her head rested on his shoulder for only a second before she turned back to their unwilling audience.

'Catherine and I have been getting to know one another,' she said, holding on to one of his hands with both of hers. 'Have you been working hard this morning, darling?'

Before Jared could reply, Catherine got to her feet. 'If you'll excuse me, I'll go and dress,' she said, and without waiting for their compliance, she exchanged a smile with Laura, gathered up her belongings and left the poolside. As she entered the house, she heard Laura say: 'Isn't she a sweet girl, Jared? And all alone in the world!'

Until then this contingency had not occurred to Catherine. She had never been a particularly dependent person, and since her father's death there had always been Tony. She sighed, stamping her bare feet as she made her way upstairs. Oh, well, Jared would no doubt disabuse Laura of that belief! Even now, he was probably confiding that 'Miss Fulton' was anything but *sweet*, and was about to pay the penalty.

Despite her assertion that she could manage to unpack her own cases, in her absence someone had done it for her, hanging her belongings away in the cedar-scented units, setting out her perfumes and cosmetics on the vanity unit.

Catherine spent some time deciding what to wear for

lunch, and it was almost one o'clock when she went down-stairs again, tall and elegant in a backless dress of swinging silk jersey that exactly matched the colour of her eyes. Cork-soled wedged sandals adding inches to her height gave her confidence, and she sauntered out on to the patio to join the others. But the pool area was deserted, and her en-trance was lost on the tiny sugar-bird, hopping about the glass-topped table searching for crumbs.

She turned back into the house, and encountered Lily in the morning room.

'You looking for the family?' the old servant inquired, and Catherine nodded. 'They're taking cocktails in the library, Miz Fulton. You know where that is?'

'I—no.'

Catherine shook her head and with an understanding smile, Lily beckoned for her to follow. Out in the hall, they turned through an arched way leading to the opposite wing of the house from that which Catherine had seen so far. Double doors to a book-lined room stood wide to admit the maximum amount of air, and she could see Elizabeth and Laura seated together on a straight-backed settee, while Jared was standing by the open windows, staring out on to the sweep of drive at the front of the building.

Elizabeth was first to look up, and with a dismissing nod towards Lily she rose to her feet and said: 'I've just sent Susie to look for you, Catherine. We thought you must have fallen asleep again.'

Catherine absorbed this without comment, and Laura stood up, too, and exclaimed: 'What a pretty dress, Cath-erine! It's the colour of those African violets Mummy cultivates at home. You've seen them, haven't you, Jared? Don't you think Catherine's dress is the same colour?'

Jared had turned with evident reluctance, but Catherine

56

met his gaze squarely. If he already thought the worst of her, it might be fun to augment that opinion. What did she have to lose?

'I don't think Miss Fulton is interested in what I think, Laura,' he was saying now, but Catherine chose to differ.

'A girl always likes to know if she's looking her best, Jared,' she insisted silkily, and was rewarded by his darkening expression.

'Will you have a drink before lunch, Catherine?'

Elizabeth's intervention was smooth and deliberate, successfully cutting off any interchange which might have developed between them, diverting attention to herself. She was wearing another of her long hostess gowns, a feminine garment, much different from the masculine lines of her riding breeches. Catherine wondered idly if she ever wore skirts.

Laura, who had apparently noticed nothing amiss, exclaimed: 'Yes, Catherine, do have a cocktail. Jared mixes them himself, and they're delicious!'

'Then I must try one, mustn't I?' said Catherine, avoiding looking at Jared, but acutely aware that he was looking at her.

'Would you like another, Laura?' Elizabeth handed Catherine a glass frosted with ice cubes. 'I think Lily must be almost ready for us.'

'No, thanks.' Laura uttered a little giggle. 'I don't want an unsteady hand this afternoon. You are coming to watch, aren't you, Jared?'

Catherine sipped her cocktail experimentally. It was delicious, as Laura had said, and she probed her palate with her tongue trying to distinguish what it was made from. She had expected rum in some form, but it wasn't that. There was whisky—and orange juice—and something else . . .

57

'But, Jared, you *promised*!'

Realising she was missing out on the conversation, Catherine endeavoured to catch up on what was going on.

'Jared does have this commission to finish, Laura.' That was Elizabeth in her gently reproving role. 'You know it isn't always possible for him to spend a whole afternoon—'

'But it's only once a year! And it's the first time I've got as far as the semi-finals!'

Catherine frowned. The semi-finals of what? What was that Laura had said about needing a steady hand? It couldn't be swimming, could it? Diving perhaps? Or riding? There seemed a strong interest in horses around here.

'Perhaps Catherine would like to go and watch you, Laura.' Elizabeth again, and Catherine raised her eyebrows helplessly. 'You like tennis, don't you, Catherine?' She was persistent, but at least now Catherine knew what they were talking about.

'I—well, sometimes,' she conceded.

'It's the club tournament finals this afternoon,' explained Laura, disappointment bringing a droop to her shoulders. 'We organise a competition every year, and this is the first time I've got so far.'

'How exciting!' Catherine tried to sound enthusiastic. Then she looked straight at Jared, astounded to find herself in the position of needing to defend his fiancée! 'And you're not going?'

'Jared's working——' began Elizabeth, but Catherine interrupted her:

'Can't Jared speak for himself?'

'Oh, please . . .'

That was Laura, her face flushed with embarrassment, but Catherine ignored her. It suddenly seemed clear why Elizabeth had no objections to Laura as a future wife for her stepson. Between them, they could reduce her to a jelly!

'It's true.' Obviously Jared did not care for having to explain himself to her, but short of ignoring her altogether, there was nothing else he could do. 'I do have to work this afternoon. I'm sorry, but there it is.'

'You had time to go down to the beach this morning!'

Her accusing tones made Elizabeth catch her breath, and Jared's jaw clenched. 'Yes, I did.'

'It doesn't matter . . .'

Laura again, and this time Catherine listened to her. It was a pointless argument anyway. Laura was apparently prepared to let him get away with it, so why should she care? All the same, she guessed that by taking Laura's part she had succeeded in antagonising Elizabeth still further. It was a relief when lunch was announced, and they could all adjourn to the dining room.

The meal was a silent one. Jared was grim and morose, Elizabeth, cold and disapproving, and Laura miserably pandering to both of them. Catherine was irritated by the girl's humility, and couldn't wait to escape to her room. She ate melon without enjoying it, concentrating on her surroundings, unwillingly admiring the dark wood furniture, and magnolia damask walls. A low chandelier was suspended above the long polished table, but Catherine guessed that on special occasions they would light the pair of silver candelabra which stood on either end of the carved sideboard. She could imagine the mellow light from candles, reflected in dark surfaces, throwing the portrait above the mantel into relief. Her gaze lingered on that painting of a woman little more than Elizabeth's age, a dark-haired woman, wearing a white gauze gown, and strings of pearls, and bearing a distinct resemblance to Jared. Could it be a painting of his mother? And if so, who had done it? Her father had told her that Jared's own mother had died when he was in his teens, so it could hardly have been him. But it was good, very good, and when she returned her attention to the table, she realised that he had observed her interest. Nevertheless, neither the painting, nor the moist and succulent fish, stuffed with vegetables and herbs, cooked in wine, and served with a crisp side salad, could entirely take away the taste of bitterness in her mouth.

But Elizabeth wasn't finished with her yet. 'I think it would be a good idea if you did go along to the club with Laura, Catherine,' she announced, when the main dishes had been taken away, and bowls of fruit and dishes of cheese had replaced them. There was still an edge of coldness to her voice, but Laura clearly saw it as the break in the ice.

'Yes. Why don't you come along, Catherine?' she exclaimed eagerly, glad of anything to ease the situation. 'I've brought my gear with me, and I'm driving over there straight after lunch.'

Catherine's palms pressed hard against her knees. Her position was hopeless, and she knew it. She looked up and encountered Jared's eyes upon her from across the width of the table, and the malicious amusement in their depths made her want to hurt him very badly.

'It will give you an opportunity to meet some other young people.' Elizabeth warmed to her theme. 'Jared and I both have work to do this afternoon, and you'd only be bored sitting here alone.'

Catherine felt like saying that she would be the best judge of what would bore her and what would not, but in spite of her contempt for Laura, she could not hurt her.

'Where is this tournament?' she asked resignedly, and knew she had taken the first irrevocable step.

'At the Alora Beach Tennis Club,' answered Laura at

once. 'It's about half an hour's drive from here. It's a super place! You can play tennis or squash; swim, if you like. And there's a children's paddling pool, and the clubhouse.'

Catherine thought it sounded exactly the sort of place she would prefer to avoid, and for the first time felt a twinge of sympathy with Jared. Somehow she didn't think he would enjoy that kind of stereotyped gathering either. But that still didn't excuse his behaviour.

'You will come, won't you?' Laura was endearingly eager, and Catherine gave in.

'I—all right.'

'Oh, wonderful!'

Laura looked delighted, and even Elizabeth was visibly thawing. 'You'll enjoy it,' she said, permitting herself a look in Jared's direction, and intercepting that brief exchange, Catherine decided that they thought they had won the unequal contest.

In the event, it was not an unpleasing afternoon.

The tennis club was by no means the institution she had expected it to be. Situated on the coast south of the Royal estate, its low buildings sprawled over several acres. There were plenty of cars parked inside the iron gates, and concrete walkways between the tennis courts leading to the swimming and paddling pools which were almost on the beach, and adjacent to the colonial styling of the clubhouse. The final stages of the tennis competition were not due to begin until four o'clock, and Laura introduced Catherine to a crowd of young people grouped beside the pool in various stages of undress.

Laura was greeted warmly, but it was apparent from the curious glances cast around that everyone wondered where Jared had got to.

'He's not coming,' Laura explained, no doubt wanting to get it over as soon as possible, and drowned their exclamations of *'The beast!'* and *'What a shame!'* with the assertion that his work was more important than a game of tennis. Watching her, Catherine realised that she really meant what she said, a fact which would have pleased Elizabeth Royal enormously.

While Laura was making apologies for Jared, a good-looking man in swimming shorts, with brown hair and the bluest eyes Catherine had ever seen, got up and offered her his seat. Thanking him, she subsided into it. It was very hot, much hotter than she was used to, and not even the thin dress she was wearing could prevent little trickles of dampness all over her body. He sat down cross-legged on the stone apron beside her, and looking up, said: 'Are you staying in Barbados long, Catherine?'

Catherine smiled. 'About six months, I think. I'm sorry —I don't remember your name.'

'John—John Dexter.' He grinned in return. 'And you're from England?'

'Yes. London, actually. I'm staying with—the Royals.'

'Yes, we had heard you were coming,' remarked John, nodding. 'Laura told us.'

'Oh.' Catherine fanned herself with one hand. 'Isn't it hot?'

John shook his head. 'Not particularly. You should take a dip in the pool and cool off. That's what I've been doing.'

'I wish I could.' Catherine was serious. 'But I haven't brought a swimsuit.'

'I could lend you one.' Laura had heard the tail-end of their conversation, and chimed in. 'Would you like a swim, Catherine?'

Catherine hesitated. Then: 'Why not?'

Laura smiled. 'Come on, then. I've got a locker in the clubhouse where I keep my things. I'll show you where you can change.'

'I'll be waiting.'

John's casual promise followed them across the lawns and into the club buildings, and Laura chuckled. 'It sounds like you've made a conquest already,' she said. 'But don't take him too seriously, will you? Johnny has quite a reputation.'

'I'll try not to,' murmured Catherine dryly, but Laura missed her sarcasm.

The water in the pool was the warmest Catherine had ever swum in, and with several of the young men competing with John for her attention, it was not difficult to convince herself that she was glad she had come. Laura's navy swimsuit fitted her quite well, and by the time she emerged to watch the competition, she felt several degrees cooler.

Unfortunately for Laura, she was knocked out of the tournament in her leg of the semi-finals. However, the girl who beat her went on to win, which assuaged her disappointment somewhat. They drove back to Amaryllis in the cooler air of early evening, but when they reached the house, Catherine left Laura to relate the events of the afternoon to her future husband and his stepmother, while she sought the welcome isolation of her room.

Dinner proved to be a non-event, even though Catherine had spent some time deciding what to wear. Only Elizabeth joined her in the lamplit dining room, the chandelier having been waived in favour of a less revealing light. When Catherine ventured to ask where Jared was, she was told, rather irritably she felt, that he was out for the evening, dining with his future in-laws. So Laura had got her fiancé to herself at last, she thought wryly. With or without Elizabeth's consent?

After the rather eventful day, Catherine slept soundly that

night, and awakened much later the next morning. An examination of her watch revealed that it was already after eight o'clock, and she lay for several minutes recalling what she had been doing at this time yesterday morning. As she got out of bed and padded into the bathroom, she wondered if Jared had gone surfing this morning, if he had taken the direct route across the fields which she had denied him the day before.

Showered, she dressed in blue denim jeans rolled back to the knee, and a striped halter top. Underneath, she wore the pants of a green bikini, and she looked forward to lazing in the sun, improving the tan she had begun the day before.

Elizabeth was alone in the morning room, seated at the breakfast table, studying the financial pages of the local newspaper. She managed a cool smile when her guest appeared, surveying her with slightly raised eyebrows. She was wearing jodhpurs again, which Catherine guessed were her usual working attire.

'Good morning,' she remarked casually, as Catherine came to sit at the table. 'You look—very well.'

It was an ambiguous comment, and Catherine realised it was the first time since her arrival that Elizabeth had seen her in anything so revealing. Did the older woman's eyes linger on the bare expanse of her midriff? Had Jared told his stepmother what she had told him, and if so, why didn't she mention it?

'It's another lovely day,' Catherine said now, smiling at Susie, who had come to attend to her needs. 'Oh, just toast and coffee, please.'

'Yes.' Elizabeth folded her newspaper. 'We are lucky with the weather.'

Catherine rested her elbows on the table, cupped her chin on her hands, and smiled her acquiescence with this statement. There were a few moments' awkward silence, and then she persevered gallantly: 'I can hardly believe it's February. Just a few thousand miles and the difference is amazing!'

'Yes.' Elizabeth finished her coffee, and pushed her cup aside. Then: 'By the way, I'm afraid I shan't be able to show you the stables today. I'd forgotten, it's our dinner party this evening, and I must make an effort to get into Bridgetown later this morning. I have a hair appointment at three, so do you think you could entertain yourself?'

'Of course.' Catherine would be glad of the opportunity to do so.

'What I mean is ...' Apparently Elizabeth wasn't happy that everything had been satisfactorily explained. 'You won't—annoy Jared, will you, Catherine? I mean, he does have to work. I know he's not in at the moment——'

'Down at the beach?' Catherine's tone was dry.

'I expect so.' Elizabeth did not approve of her flippancy. 'I have explained that, Catherine.'

'Oh, you have!' Catherine's eyes were wide and innocent. 'And I understand. Don't worry, Mrs Royal. I'll just sit beside the pool and avoid making a nuisance of myself.'

Elizabeth's smile was frosty, but she rose to her feet and adjusted her chair. 'If you'll excuse me, then ...'

'Of course.' Catherine looked demure. 'Don't work too hard.'

She finished breakfast alone, and then sauntered outside. The pool looked very inviting, but she decided to allow her breakfast to digest before trying it. She had sunglasses in her pocket, so kicking off her sandals, she stretched her length on a lounger.

She had been there perhaps half an hour, and was considering going indoors for her anti-sunburn oil so that she could shed her jeans, when a man came strolling on to the patio. His booted feet sounded hollowly on the stone tiles, and she opened her eyes in surprise to find him standing a few feet away watching her.

Wriggling into an upright position, she took off her dark glasses, and said politely: 'Can I help you?'

The man grinned. He was a little above average height, stockily built, with greying fair hair, and attractively tanned features. In knee-lenth boots and riding breeches, a thin cotton shirt open over his broad chest, he looked like an old-style plantation boss, but she had no idea who he could be.

'You would be Miss Fulton, of course,' he remarked, coming nearer, revealing that he walked with a distinct limp. His accent was unmistakable, and Catherine nodded, remembering.

'And you're Mr Donovan,' she countered, swinging her feet to the ground. 'Are you looking for Elizabeth?'

It was strange how easily Elizabeth's name came to her lips when she was not actually speaking to the woman herself.

'That's right,' Patrick Donovan agreed now. 'Is she about?'

'I really don't know. Actually, I thought she had gone down to the stables.'

Donovan sighed. 'Damn! I wanted to ask her whether the buyer we had yesterday was coming back today.'

'Oh, I shouldn't think so.' Catherine rose to her feet, so that she was almost on eye-level terms with him. 'I understand she wants to go into Bridgetown this morning, and she has a hair appointment this afternoon. For a dinner party she's giving this evening.'

'Yes.' Donovan frowned. 'Well, you could be right.' Then he threw off his uncertainty. 'How are you settling down at Amaryllis?'

66

Catherine shrugged. 'I—it's all right.'

'You're not impressed.'

'I wouldn't say that exactly. But ...' She shook her head. 'Have you worked here long?'

'About ten years.'

'So you'll have known—Jared's father?'

'Sure. He employed me in the first place.'

Catherine nodded, fiddling with her glasses. 'Does—does Jared take after his father?'

'Jared?' Donovan gave her a wry look, and she wondered if she had been indiscreet. 'How do you mean?'

Catherine could feel herself colouring. 'What I mean is—is he a good boss?'

Donovan grinned. 'Do you really expect me to tell you?' Then he laughed. 'The best!'

'Why do you say it like that?'

'Because he never interferes in the business.'

'You don't mind?'

'Why should I? No, Jared's pretty shrewd in money matters, and he expects a fair return for his investment, but on the whole he leaves the running of the stables to me.'

'And—Elizabeth?'

'You ask a lot of questions, don't you?'

Catherine bent her head. 'I'm sorry. But you're the first person I've met since coming here that I've felt able to ask.'

Donovan looked at her sympathetically. 'I'll take that as a compliment,' he teased, and she laughed, relaxing again. 'As a matter of fact, Mrs Royal has a good business head on her shoulders,' he added. 'I leave the financial side of things to her. She likes paper work, and I'm no clerical assistant. She does all the buying and selling, and we both attend the bloodstock sales.'

'It sounds interesting.'

'If you like horses,' he conceded, 'and I love them. I was brought up on a farm in Ireland where they bred racehorses, and I've never forgotten the thrill I felt when my father put me up on my first mount. I must have been about three at the time, but it's stuck in my mind, you know what I mean?' He paused. 'Perhaps you'd like to see our own champion. Chartreuse! He won every big race he entered. Including the Kentucky Derby. That was a proud day!' He shook his head reminiscently. 'But now he uses his energies in another direction!'

Catherine guessed what he meant and chuckled, but her amusement faded when a harsh voice interrupted them.

'Are you looking for me, Donovan?'

Jared walked on to the patio from the direction of the tennis courts, lean and sensually disturbing in tight-fitting cotton pants that hung low on his hips. That they were damp in places revealed that he had not bothered to dry himself before getting dressed, and Catherine had to make an effort not to stare too openly.

'I was looking for Mrs Royal, sir.' Donovan turned to face his employer. 'But Miss Fulton's just been telling me she's going into town.'

'Has she?' Jared's tawny eyes flicked Catherine with cold arrogance. 'And what have you been telling her?'

Donovan looked nonplussed. 'I don't know what you mean, sir.'

'Don't you?' Jared halted before them, dark and intimidating. 'What is there about my stepmother going to town that's so amusing?'

Donovan shifted uncomfortably and Catherine felt resentment flooding her being. What was wrong with two people talking together? Why shouldn't they?

'Do you monitor all conversations on these premises?'

she inquired insolently, and was aware that Donovan did not welcome her intervention.

'I was telling Miss Fulton about Chartreuse, sir,' he put in quickly, but Jared had turned to his house guest.

'Donovan doesn't have time to stand here chatting to you!' he stated grimly. 'If you're bored, that's not his problem.'

'Nor yours, either, I suppose!' she retorted, but again Jared had transferred his attention.

'If that's all, Donovan?' he prompted authoritatively, and with an apologetic nod, the Irishman walked quickly away.

When he had gone, Catherine flung herself on to the lounger, pushing the dark glasses on to her nose and deliberately ignoring the man at her side. She stretched out her legs, positioned her arms so that they benefited most from the sun's rays, and forced a look of relaxation which she was far from feeling.

She expected Jared to leave her, not particularly caring what he thought of her right then, but when he spoke she realised she had been a fool to think she could get off so lightly.

'Don't you ever speak to me like that again in front of a member of my staff!' he told her angrily, and although Catherine quivered at the threatening note in his voice, she refused to let him see he had disturbed her.

Opening her eyes, she tilted the glasses so she could see over them, and said: 'Only when we're alone, is that right?'

Jared pushed his balled fists into the hip pockets of his pants. 'And while we're on the subject, don't interfere in matters between Laura and me!'

Catherine sat up. 'I presume you mean yesterday.'

'When else?'

'Has Laura been complaining?'

Jared glared at her. '*I'm* telling you. Mind your own business!'

Catherine swung her feet to the tiles and stood up once more, unable to stand the disadvantage of remaining seated a moment longer. 'Elizabeth doesn't,' she pointed out pleasantly.

'Elizabeth is my stepmother.'

'And I'm your ward, *guardian*! Or had you forgotten?'

'It would be impossible, wouldn't it?' he demanded harshly, and her eyes fell before the penetration of his. 'Now, for God's sake, I've got work to do!'

Catherine lifted her head. 'I'm not stopping you.'

'Aren't you?' His muttered words barely reached her, and the hand that reached out almost savagely and grasped a handful of her hair seemed motivated almost against his will. 'Is this colour real or cultivated?'

Catherine wet her upper lip with the tip of her tongue. 'It's real,' she managed, suddenly finding herself short of breath.

His eyes moved over her face with searching intensity. 'And how many men have asked that, I wonder?' he mused contemptuously.

'Not—not as many as you might think,' she murmured, willing him to stop tormenting them both and pull her into his arms, close against that lean hard body . . .

'No?' He sounded unconvinced. 'Well, whatever you are and whatever you've done, I want to paint you. Pagan motherhood! How does that appeal to you?'

Her disappointment was a physical thing, and she felt almost sick with anti-climax. For a few moments she had forgotten everything but a disturbing need for contact between them, and it was difficult now to accept that his interest had been wholly detached.

70

Playing for time, she said: 'But you haven't told anyone, have you?'

'No.' He shook his head. 'They'll find out soon enough, won't they?' His features were cold. 'Well? Will you take your clothes off for me?'

Catherine stared at him, despising the way her traitorous emotions leapt at his words. She wondered what he would do if she did just that, at this moment! He thought he had everything under control, and she would love to destroy his complacency.

But she couldn't do it, and knowing in advance what his reaction to her next words would be, she said softly: 'You can take them off yourself, if you like.'

He released her hair at once, stepping back away from her, his eyes glittering angrily. 'No, thanks,' he retorted. 'That was not what I had in mind.'

Catherine shrugged, and with great self-control, subsided on to the lounger again, pushing the dark glasses back on to her nose.

'You have no shame, do you?' he exploded, and for an instant her conscience warned her of the dangerous game she was playing. But she had gone too far now to draw back, and instead of answering him she made a little sound of lazy satisfaction as she stretched beneath the sun's rays. There was a moment's tension, when she could hear his hard breathing, and then the receding sound of his footsteps.

CHAPTER FIVE

FLOODLIT, the patio acquired an air of mystery it did not possess in daylight. Strings of coloured bulbs had been trailed along the sides of the pool, reflecting the curiosly elongated brilliance in the clear water, and the shrubs and palm trees which surrounded the area took on an eerie beauty at night. There were blossoms which only opened their petals to the moon, and they shed their distinctive fragrance to mingle with more sophisticated perfumes in the velvety evening air.

Dinner had been served at eight as usual for the Royals and a dozen of their guests, but several more couples had arrived later to join the party on the patio. Buffet tables had been set up at one side for anyone who was hungry, heavy with cold hams and salads, *vol-au-vents* and savouries, trifles, cheeses and wine, while Henry dispensed stronger drinks from an improvised bar nearby. Loudspeakers had been set up earlier in the day, and music was now being diffused over the colourful scene, encouraging some of the younger members of the party to dance.

It was the first big party Elizabeth had given since Catherine arrived on the island, and much different from the introductory dinner she had arranged almost a week ago now. Then, it had been merely a question of eating a meal and sharing a rather boring after-dinner conversation with Laura and her parents, Judge Ferris and his wife, and two young men who had obviously been invited to make up the numbers. This evening had proved to be a much less formal occasion, and the numbers involved had made conversations less personal.

The week since her arrival seemed to have passed over amazingly quickly. In spite of the fact that she had seen next to nothing of Jared, time had not hung heavily on her hands. Jared was working, shut in his studio at the top of the house, where as yet Catherine had not been permitted to go. There had been no further talk of his painting her, indeed he avoided her whenever possible, and she doubted he approved of her friendship with his fiancée.

Laura was over most days. Catherine didn't fool herself that she came to see her, even though ostensibly this was her purpose. She always hoped to encounter Jared, but when she did not, she usually suggested she and Catherine entertained each other. They had swum and played a not-very-strenuous game of tennis on the Royal courts, and once Laura had driven her into Bridgetown. But the island capital had been uncomfortably hot for sightseeing, even though the heat could not alter its old world charm, and they had spent most of the time at the Careenage, the inner harbour, where Catherine was fascinated by the tall-masted schooners, and the picturesque uniforms of the harbour police.

Elizabeth approved of their friendship, as well she might, Catherine had thought cynically. With herself keeping Laura away from her fiancé, Elizabeth had her stepson to herself.

Now Catherine was sitting in the canopied shade of a garden hammock, swinging her legs and idly listening to John Dexter extolling the delights of sailing. It had been no surprise to discover he was one of the invited dinner guests, he had rung a couple of times through the week, but while his attentiveness was flattering his conversation bored her. Andy David, another of the young men she had met at the tennis club, had already ventured to ask her to

73

dance, but she had refused him, guessing as she did so that John probably imagined that she preferred his company. But the truth was, she didn't feel like dancing right now. Sitting in the shadow of the canopy, she could observe without being observed, and her eyes lingered shamelessly on Jared.

He seemed relaxed and at ease with these people who were his friends, and it was obvious that he was popular. Most of the young women present found an excuse to stand with him or speak with him, and Laura, hovering at his side, looked proud, and rather smug that she wore his ring on her finger. Elizabeth was never far away from her stepson's side. In a long coral-coloured chiffon gown, she quite eclipsed the muted shades of Laura's blue silk sheath, and from a distance Catherine had to concede that she did not look that much older than the other girl.

Jared, who had just joined in a particularly strenuous beat session, had shed his dinner jacket for coolness. The fine white silk of his shirt clung to his back in places, and he had loosened his tie and unbuttoned the ruffled pleats below his collar. He was laughing at something someone had said, and watching him, Catherine felt a pain like a knife turn in her stomach. Why had he forced her to come here? she demanded silently, aware that by doing so he was gradually turning her normally balanced world upside-down.

'Would you like to dance?'

John's casual invitation interrupted the painful course of her thoughts, and she nodded vigorously, needing to escape from where they were leading her. They left the hammock and walked slowly into the group of people already dancing near the french windows, and John drew her possessively into his arms.

'Did I tell you I like your dress?' he murmured, his

74

cheek against hers, and she smiled.

'Several times,' she conceded, her eyes unwillingly seeking a certain pair of broad shoulders.

'I mean it.' John's hand in the small of her back tightened. 'Not every girl could wear brown and get away with it.'

Catherine suppressed a laugh. 'It's not actually brown,' she corrected him. 'It's cinnamon. But thank you all the same.'

In truth, she had hesitated some time over wearing this particular gown with its caped, off-the-shoulder bodice, and softly moulded skirt because of the colour. But instead of looking drab, as she had thought it might, with her hair and the gently toning tan she was acquiring, it stood out among so many vivid colours with a subdued elegance.

'I wanted to ask you—would you come sailing with me one day?' John drew back to look into her face, and Catherine met his gaze thoughtfully.

'Maybe,' she said, and as she did so, she encountered Jared's eyes upon her, dark and brooding in the muted light. He was dancing with Elizabeth to the slow, haunting strains of Michel Legrand's 'What are you doing the rest of your life?' and something in the music made Catherine do something she might never have dared to do otherwise.

She turned out of John's arms, and tapping Elizabeth on the shoulder said: 'Take pity on poor John, will you, Mrs Royal? He's absolutely dying to dance with you.' And before any of them could offer a protest, she had interposed herself between Jared and his stepmother, and short of causing an unpleasant scene, there was nothing any of them could do. Her hands slid up Jared's shirt front to his shoulders, but with a tightening of his lips, he took hold of them with one of his, and holding her at arm's-length, he began to dance.

'Oh, Jared!' she exclaimed, aware that other eyes were watching them, and after a moment's hesitation, he freed her, allowing them to dance normally. But there was still too much distance between them, and she moved closer, fighting his efforts to thwart her.

'You amaze me, you really do!' he muttered, but there was a hoarse note in his voice which had not been there before, and his breath was warm against her temple.

Taking advantage of his weakening, she pressed herself against him, and with a groan, his arms slid right round her, holding her with all the strength and power she had known him capable of. They moved languidly in time with the music, a sensual, sexual experience, and Catherine's sleeves fell back as her arms encircled his neck. She wished the music would go on for ever, that she could always feel the stirring hardness of his body arousing hers to a deeper awareness of her own femininity. She didn't care in those moments who was watching them or what interpretation might be put on her behaviour, and somehow she didn't think Jared cared too much either.

Eventually, the tempo of the music changed, but instead of letting her go as she had expected, he swung her into the faster rhythm, sending her spinning away from him, and then catching her hand as she turned and bringing her close against him again. It was as exhilarating as the previous music had been seductive, and Catherine's lips parted as her breathing quickened, laughing into his intent face and bringing a reluctant glimmer of admiration to his eyes. Several of the other guests began to clap their hands in time to the beat, willing to watch what was obviously to be an exhibition, and out of the corner of her eye Catherine could see Elizabeth and John joining the group surrounding them.

But for once Jared was indifferent to onlookers. He was

good, she had known that when she watched him earlier, but even she was surprised at the ease with which he matched his step to hers, revealing a mastery of the rhythm which hinted at a darker strain in his ancestry. Catherine was breathless when the music finally ended, and collapsed against her partner after one final dizzying spin. Jared's arms came round to support her automatically, but then Laura was at his side, determined to be the first to congratulate them, and he was forced to let Catherine go.

'That was super, darling!' she exclaimed, immediately reducing what had been a violent emotional experience to mediocrity, and Catherine turned frustratedly away from them, ignoring the words of admiration that rang in her ears from all sides. She wanted to escape, to get away from these people, but John Dexter was beside her, and his reactions were anything but congratulatory.

'What the hell do you mean by unloading me on to Jared's old lady?' he demanded, grasping her arm, and holding up her head, she faced him defiantly.

'Did I do that?'

'You know you did.' John raked an angry hand through his hair. 'What is it with you? Jared's Laura's property, or didn't you know?'

Catherine moved out of earshot of the group surrounding Jared. 'And what am I supposed to have done, for heaven's sake?' she exclaimed impatiently.

'Don't give me that!' John's jaw clenched and unclenched. 'You know what you did as well as I do.'

'We danced, that was all. Danced!'

'Danced!' John's echo of the word was a growl. 'I can think of other descriptions.'

'And what gives you the right to question what I do?' she asked peremptorily.

John kicked moodily at the bole of a nearby palm.

'Nothing,' he said reluctantly. 'Nothing, except that I—well, I don't want to see you get hurt, Catherine.'

Catherine stared at him disbelievingly. 'I'm not that green, John.'

'Well, all right. I was jealous,' he muttered, and the humour in the situation brought a faint smile to her lips.

'I don't somehow think you'd get much sympathy from Elizabeth if she knew you'd called her Jared's old lady,' she murmured with some amusement, and saw his teeth glinting in the shadows.

'No,' he conceded wryly. 'You could be right.'

'So ...' Catherine indicated that the music had started again. 'Do you want to dance some more?'

John regarded her steadily. 'With you?'

'Yes. With me.' Catherine glanced round. 'Before—before Jared's old lady comes looking for me.' She paused, and he drew her into his arms on the dancing area. 'Was she—very annoyed?'

'She hid it well,' he answered, grinning. 'Or maybe she really did want to dance with me.'

Catherine laughed softly. Suddenly John was a much nicer person, and she realised that his trouble was that none of the girls he had dated had robbed him so successfully of his conceit.

Across the patio, Jared was standing with Laura and her parents, and Catherine forced herself not to watch them. She wondered what they were saying, whether they, like Laura, had ignored the deeper implications of what had happened on the dance floor. Because Catherine could not. Whatever she had told John, she knew that things could never be quite the same between her and Jared, although this was not necessarily a good thing. John was right, after all. He was not her property. So why couldn't she believe that he was Laura's?

She sighed, and John said: 'Now what is it?' in anxious tones, but she just shook her head, and her smile reassured him.

She didn't see Elizabeth again to speak to until the last of their guests was leaving. It was after two o'clock, and a feeling of dejection had replaced her earlier euphoria. She longed to go to bed, to seek the silent darkness beneath the sheets, and submerge herself in the fantasy world of oblivion. Jared had departed over an hour ago to take Laura home, and when the last car disappeared down the drive, she and Elizabeth were alone.

Out on the patio, two of the servants who had been asked to work late were busily collecting glasses, loading uneaten food on to trays, and tossing soiled napkins into the waste bin. By morning, nothing would remain of the night's festivities, and Catherine could see a certain similarity between this tangible chaos and her intangible emotions.

In the hall, Elizabeth surveyed her stepson's charge coldly, tilting back her head and adopting an arrogance that any member of royalty might have envied. 'I realise this is neither the time nor the place to bring this up,' she said, and Catherine wondered why people felt the need to say such a thing when they obviously intended going ahead anyway, 'but I have to tell you that your behaviour this evening disgusted me, Catherine.'

'I'm sorry.'

Catherine didn't pretend not to understand what she meant, and Elizabeth was mildly disconcerted. 'Are you?' A handful of seconds ticked away. 'I can't altogether believe that. What you did, you did—deliberately, calculatedly, knowing how you would hurt Laura by your actions——'

'That's not true!'

'What's not true? Of course you hurt——'

'I didn't mean that,' Catherine broke in quietly. 'That

part about it being deliberate and calculating—it wasn't. It was reckless, if you like—impulsive, maybe. But that's all.'

'Really? And how do you think Jared felt? Among all his friends? A guest in this house behaving in such a—a crude and—wanton way!'

'Now wait a minute——'

'No, you wait a minute, Catherine. I don't know what kind of society you were brought up in in England, but here we have a different code of values.'

'Do you?'

'Yes.' Elizabeth's lips curled. 'We don't throw ourselves at a man who so obviously finds our presence an unnecessary encumbrance!'

'An unnecessary encumbrance!' Catherine echoed the words on a gasp. 'You can't honestly believe that!'

Elizabeth's brow creased. 'What do you mean?'

Catherine's cheeks were pale but determined. 'What do you think I mean?' She tilted her head. 'You can't believe that Jared didn't *enjoy* it!'

'What the *hell* is going on here?' Jared's voice grated harshly in the sudden stillness. They had been so intent on their arguing that they had not heard the sound of his car returning, but now he stood regarding them angrily, his white dinner jacket draped carelessly over one shoulder, dark trousers moulding the taut muscles of his thighs. 'Well?' he demanded. 'Are you aware that your voices must be audible clear to the ocean? For God's sake, if you must bitch at one another, do it somewhere less public!'

Elizabeth gathered the folds of her gown about her. 'I was merely pointing out the unsuitability of Catherine's behaviour this evening, Jared,' she said, with dignity. 'Any—*bitching*—that was going on was not at my instigation.'

'I should have thought the only person liable to be offended by our behaviour this evening was Laura,' Jared

80

retorted coldly.

'Oh, *Laura*!'

Elizabeth's tone was scornful, and Jared's expression hardened. 'Yes, Laura,' he repeated steadily. 'At no time have I appointed you my keeper, Liz!'

Elizabeth cast a venomous look in Catherine's direction. 'Are you telling me you approve of the exhibition she gave this evening?' she exclaimed bitterly, and Catherine wondered what she would do if Jared chose this moment to reveal his supposed knowledge of her physical condition. What weapon to put into his stepmother's hands! But she would never forgive him if he did.

Jared merely shook his head, however, tossing his dinner jacket in a heap on a carved chair which stood near the foot of the stairs. 'I think the less said about that, the better,' he intoned grimly, striding towards the arched entrance to the left wing of the house. 'Go to bed'— his gaze licked coldly over Catherine as well as Elizabeth,—'both of you!'

But of course when Catherine did reach the sanctuary of her room, sleep was elusive. The exhaustion she had felt in bidding goodbye to their guests had been dissipated in that scene with Elizabeth, and now her mind felt sharp and alert.

She paced restlessly about her bedroom in her striped cotton nightshirt. It was a current craze in England to wear men's nightshirts instead of nightdresses, but Catherine had always found them more comfortable than conventional night attire.

Now she pushed open the balcony doors and stood for a few minutes looking down on to the patio. Only the lights remained to be extinguished, and even as she watched the area was plunged into darkness. Now the servants could go to bed and the house could settle down for the night. She sighed, leaning her bare arms upon the balcony rail. It was

81

so warm, and faintly on the breeze she could hear the murmur of the ocean. If only it was nearer she could have gone swimming. The only other occasion she had ever swum at night had been at a barbecue in Italy, and then there had been dozens of other people around, not the silent isolation she was presently seeking. But in any case, it was a useless longing. The beach was miles away. Even so ...

Suddenly, in the darkness below her, the glow of a cigar burned brightly for a moment, and she realised that Jared was down there. She frowned, trying to distinguish his whereabouts, and felt a sense of shock when she discovered he was staring up towards her balcony. She drew back hastily into the shadows, but his voice came softly on the night air.

'It's too late. I know you're there.'

Catherine hesitated a moment and then stepped back to the rail. 'What are you doing?'

As her eyes accustomed themselves to the darkness she saw him shrug his shoulders. 'Just taking a stroll before——' He broke off, lifting his head, the planes of his face shadowed and enigmatic. 'Can't you sleep?'

She couldn't tell whether he really cared or otherwise, but she shook her head. 'No.'

'I don't suppose you're worrying about what Liz said to you, are you?'

Catherine scuffed her bare toes. 'Not a lot.'

'I thought not.' His tone was dry. 'Nevertheless, be assured, it won't happen again.'

'Won't it?' Catherine's voice was almost inaudible, but his retort was not: *'No!'*

Catherine's palm caressed the stone balustrade. 'Do you know what I was just thinking?' He made no reply and she went on softly: 'I was thinking how lovely it must be to go swimming at night.'

There was silence for so long that if she had not been able to see the shadowy figure there below her she might have thought he had gone indoors. But at last he said in a harsh voice: 'Have you any idea of the scandal there would be if we were discovered doing such a thing?'

Catherine's breath caught in her throat. 'Is that an invitation, Jared?'

He swore softly. 'No, damn you, it's not!'

'But if—if I asked you ...'

His booted toe ground over the stub of his cheroot. 'No, Catherine.'

It was the first time she had heard him use her name, and she liked it on his lips. She would like to hear him say it when he was making love to her ...

'Jared?'

'You're crazy, do you know that?'

'Shall I get dressed?'

'Don't you mean undressed?' He shifted impatiently, rubbing the back of his neck with one ungentle hand. 'God, Catherine, I have work to do tomorrow! Do you have any idea what time it is?'

'Hmm—mmm. It's about three o'clock.'

'Three-twelve, to be precise,' he muttered, consulting the plain gold watch on his wrist.

'So?'

'Oh, come down,' he said savagely. 'I'll get the bike. I've no intention of getting the car out again tonight. Can you—I mean—will you be able to ride the bike?'

'Of course.' She smiled, excitement bubbling inside her. 'I won't be five minutes.'

He didn't answer, striding into the house and disappearing from her view.

Her fingers fumbled over the strap of her white bikini, but at last it was secured and she pulled on blue jeans and a soft blue wool sweater. She confined her hair with an elastic band, and carrying her sandals left the room.

The house was in darkness, but as she hesitated in the hall, Jared came through one of the arched ways. His expression was hidden in shadow, but he beckoned for her to follow him, and they went back the way he had come, and out through a side door Catherine had never used before.

Outside, they walked round to the front of the building and she saw the gleam of metal indicating that Jared had left the motor-cycle on the drive. They walked halfway to the gates before Jared swung his leg across the bike and gestured that she should join him. Holding on to his shoulders, she did so, and when she was comfortably settled he started the engine.

The night air was cool, but not cold, and Catherine slid her arms round his middle, resting her cheek against his back. He had put on his dinner jacket again, and she wondered what could be more incongruous than anyone riding a motor-bike in evening dress.

They turned south on the coast road, instead of north towards Flintlock, but Catherine didn't risk shouting her obvious question. Jared knew where he was going, and quite honestly, she would have been content to ride with him all night.

He eventually stopped beside a grassy slope leading down to sand-dunes where the roar of the ocean was a much gentler sound than at Flintlock. He switched off the ignition, and Catherine climbed rather stiffly off her seat.

'Are you all right?' he asked, still astride the bike, and she nodded, smiling.

'Just stiff. It's years since I rode a motor-bike.'

Jared regarded her intently for several seconds, and then with a faint shrug, he dismounted, supporting the bike on its metal stand. He removed his jacket and laid it over the handlebars, and then indicated the dunes. 'Go ahead.'

A pale moon illuminated the beach, wild and lonely, and to Catherine, incredibly beautiful. Clumps of palms scraped a living amongst the dunes, and long-stemmed grasses were dark against the sand. She left her sandals beside the bike, loving the feeling of the tiny coral grains between her toes. Several yards away, the sea creamed in a white line along the shore, and she longed to feel its soft caress over her heated limbs.

She turned back and found Jared behind her, dark and thoughtful in the pale light. He was still fully dressed, and she plucked doubtfully at the wool of her sweater.

'Are you—coming in?' she asked.

Jared looked down at her. 'After you,' he said evenly.

'*After* me?'

'The last time I brought you to the beach, your bathing suit never got wet,' he reminded her.

Catherine sighed. 'That was—different.'

'How different?'

'You didn't want to bring me then,' she told him softly.

'And this time I did?'

'Well, didn't you?'

He turned away, stripping off his shirt. 'Let's swim,' he said flatly, and taking off his trousers, he walked towards the water.

She had expected him to have changed at the house, but he swam in navy blue underpants, leaving her to take off her clothes and follow him. She hesitated only a moment before doing so, and then with an eagerness she could not disguise, she tugged off her pants and sweater and ran towards the waves.

They were just as soft and delightful as she had anticipated, and she swam lazily out from the shore, her arms making little sound in the water. She could see a dark head

85

some distance out from the beach, but the sea-bed shelved rather rapidly, and she remained closer in to shore. Turning on to her back, she floated for a while, trying to distinguish the composition of stars in the night sky, but all the while conscious of Jared only feet away from her. She wondered what Elizabeth would do if she discovered Jared's bed was empty. Would she look to see if Catherine was in her room? Might she think they could be there together? And if she found they were both missing . . .

Catherine turned over and began to swim again. She didn't want to think about Elizabeth. Doing so led inevitably to Laura, and the cruel way she was treating her. Why was she doing this? She wasn't naturally a selfish girl. But when she was with Jared everything—and every*body*— else faded into insignificance.

It was only as she was wading up out of the water that she realised she had brought no towel to dry herself. She ran her hands down her arms, brushing away the surplus moisture and almost jumped out of her skin when a lazy hand curled round her ankle. She had been unaware that Jared had already left the water, and to find him stretched out on the sand almost at her feet brought the blood surging to the surface of her skin.

'I—haven't got a towel,' she said jerkily.

'Nor have I,' he responded, looking up at her with disturbing intensity. 'Come here and I'll dry you.'

'H—how?'

'I'll show you.' His hand slid up to her knee. 'Come here . . .'

Absurdly, she hesitated. 'No, I—I'll get my clothes . . .'

'Why?' With a lithe movement he was on his feet beside her. 'I'd only have to take them off again.'

'Jared——'

'Yes?'

'Jared ...' Her breathing was constricted. He was standing so close that his legs were touching hers. And where they touched, little rivers of fire started along her veins. 'Are—are you sure?'

He was shaking his head as his arms slid around her, moving possessively over her hips, moulding her yielding body to the thrusting hardness of his. 'I'm not sure of anything any more,' he groaned into the nape of her neck. 'But this is good, isn't it? Tell me it's good.'

'It's ... good,' she managed chokingly, and grasping his face between her two hands she brought his mouth to hers.

Even she had been unprepared for the urgency which engulfed them. All evening she had been waiting for this—all the time they had been dancing—possessing each other in every way except the physical one—she had been living for this moment, and from the way Jared was holding her, she knew he had been waiting for the same. Her lips parted wide beneath his, and she felt his passionate exploration of the moistness within. His hands probed every inch of her spine, sliding under the weight of her hair and tugging it free of the offending elastic band so that he could wind its wet coils round his fingers. Without lifting his head, he drew her down on to the sand beside him, using his weight as a potent stimulant to her overheated emotions.

'God, I want you,' he breathed, in the hollow between her breasts, and she felt the fastening of the bikini bra give beneath the pressure he was exerting. His mouth sought the rose-tinted peaks exposed to his gaze, and Catherine's lower limbs were aching for a satisfaction only he could give her. 'You're so beautiful,' he muttered roughly, and when his hungry mouth sought hers again, she wound her arms round his neck, holding him closer.

Catherine's skin had dried rapidly, but there was a film of sand clinging abrasively to her bare back. Jared's lovemaking had a certain abrasiveness, too, wild and primitive, their almost naked bodies fusing together, limbs entangled, his mouth seeking and possessing, awakening her to an awareness of her own vulnerability where this man was concerned.

It was Jared who broke their embrace, rolling away from her to stretch his length on the sand, both hands pressed to his temples. His features were taut with the effort of controlling his emotions, and his hoarse: 'In God's name, what am I doing?' was both a torment and an accusation.

'Jared——' Catherine began huskily, but he got violently to his feet, reaching automatically for his pants.

'Cover yourself!' he muttered savagely, turning away from her, and she fastened her bra with trembling fingers.

'What's the matter?' she cried, getting to her knees and staring up at him. 'What's wrong?'

'What's wrong?' His laugh was harsh. 'My God, you know what's wrong! I forgot, do you believe that? I *really* forgot that I wasn't the first man to——' He broke off, his mouth twisting contemptuously. 'Oh, no, Catherine,' he intoned brutally, 'you're not going to use me to shed doubt about the fatherhood of that child you're carrying——'

'But I'm not——'

It was out before she could retract it, but Jared paid her words no heed. 'Forget it! I want no part of a deal like that!' He buttoned his shirt with hands which were not quite steady. 'You really had me going there for a minute,' he muttered, angry with himself as well as with her. 'Oh, for God's sake, Catherine, get your clothes on! We're going back. Right now. I just hope to hell no one's noticed our absence.'

'Like Elizabeth, for instance?'

A coldness which was as much mental as physical was filling her, and she didn't much care what she said just at that moment.

Jared's brows drew together. 'Why mention Elizabeth?'

'Why not?' Catherine pulled her sweater over her head, with a casualness she was far from feeling. 'I'd have thought she was the most obvious person.'

Jared's expression was grim. 'What the hell are you implying?'

Catherine shrugged, stepping carelessly into her jeans. 'I'm sorry,' but her tone implied otherwise, 'I just thought she might have—well, gone to tuck her little boy up for the night!'

She knew at once that she had gone too far. Jared reached for her furiously, and only by jack-knifing backwards did she succeed in evading him. With her heart thumping rapidly in her ears, and a sob of hysteria rising in her throat, she turned and ran up the beach and across the sand-dunes to where Jared had left the motor-bike. At any moment she expected to hear him behind her. His long legs would outstrip hers in any race they cared to run, and her escape could only be a postponement of what was surely to come.

She reached the motor-bike and glanced fearfully over her shoulder. Jared was still some distance away from her, following without haste, but with a relentless persistence which seemed that much more threatening. He thought she was trapped here. He had no need to hurry. If she ran, he would catch her easily on the motor-bike.

The motor-bike!

Catherine turned to it urgently. It was bigger than the two-stroke she had ridden back home, but basically the controls were the same. And the keys were in the ignition.

Before he could hazard her intentions and put on sufficient speed to prevent her, she had swung her leg across the seat, thrown his jacket down, and started the engine.

The noise was deafening, but she still heard his angry exclamation, and that was enough to compel her forward. With a few jerky accelerations, she was off the grass and on to the road, and then it was plain sailing. A laugh of pure delight escaped her as she glanced back over her shoulder once and saw Jared standing in the middle of the road staring after her. Oh, glory, she thought unrepentantly, she had really done it now!

CHAPTER SIX

It was after eleven when Catherine was awakened next morning, and then it was to find Susie standing beside her bed holding a tray of fruit juice and coffee. The curiously ominous feeling of apprehension that awaited her return to consciousness had nothing to do with the smiling face of the serving girl, and she struggled up on to her pillows and thanked Susie for her thoughtfulness.

'Miz Prentiss is downstairs,' the girl explained apologetically, setting the legs of the tray across Catherine's knees. 'I told her you will be very tired, but she said you'd want to be up now.'

Catherine gave her an understanding smile. 'That's all right, Susie. Miss Prentiss is right anyway—I ought to be up. I—where is everyone else?'

'Miz Royal is down at the stables, Miz Fulton. And Mr Royal—he's not here.'

'Not here?' Catherine couldn't prevent the automatic rejoinder.

'No, Miz Fulton.'

'Then where is he?' Memories of Jared standing alone in the middle of that lonely road came back to torment her. Nothing had happened to him, had it? She would never forgive herself ... 'I—have you seen him this morning?'

Susie regarded her curiously. 'Yes, Miz Fulton.' She paused, frowning. 'You want to see him?'

Catherine wondered how much of what had happened last night had filtered through to the kitchen. Probably enough to arouse conjecture among the other servants. It would not do to supplement that speculation by revealing so intent an interest in Jared's affairs.

'Not now, Susie,' she said quickly, hoping to divert the girl. 'Mmm, this looks appetising. How did you know I wouldn't want anything to eat?'

'I don't know, miz.' Susie looked pleased. 'Shall I tell Miz Prentiss you'll be down directly?'

'Yes, you do that.' Catherine forced a lightness to her tone. 'Where is she?'

'On the patio, Miz Fulton. I'll tell her.'

After the maid had left, Catherine put the tray aside and slid out of bed. Surreptitiously, she opened the balcony doors which she had locked the night before, half afraid that Jared might use this method to try and reach her after he got back. But she had fallen asleep without hearing anyone enter the house.

Laura was sitting disconsolately on one of the colourful loungers, watching Henry disconnecting coloured bulbs from the trees around the pool area. Her body was hunched, spine curved, elbows resting on her knees, chin cupped in her palms. She looked low and dejected, and Catherine felt the full weight of her own treachery. Whatever Jared's motives for abandoning their lovemaking the night before, the end result had achieved something which she should have wanted in the first place. She didn't know what had possessed her, and the memory of that abandoned embrace brought the blood rushing to the surface of her skin all over her body. She guessed she had destroyed any faint hope of convincing him that she was not the free-loving individual he thought her, but in the circumstances, perhaps that was just as well. What had begun as a game had drastically altered, and although sooner or later he was bound to discover she was not pregnant, he would doubtless consider that to be more good luck than management. What an awful cliché that was, she thought disgustedly. But it contained the essential truth of the situation, and she had no one but herself to blame ...

With a sigh, she poured herself a glass of freshly-squeezed orange juice, and carried it into the bathroom. A warm shower cleansed the salt from her hair and her skin. The night before, she had only taken the time to rub her hair almost dry with a towel before tumbling into bed, but now she emerged feeling fresher, and more ready to face the day.

She dressed in a simple halter-necked shift, and secured her still damp hair in a ponytail with a sea-green ribbon, the exact colour of her dress. Eye-shadow did not take long to apply, and her honey-tanned skin required no further adornment. With dark glasses swinging from her hand, she felt remarkably composed as she went downstairs, but this soon dissipated beneath Laura's reproachful stare.

'Hello, Catherine,' she greeted her coolly. 'You must have been tired.'

'I was.' Catherine lifted the glasses as if to put them on her nose, and then let them fall again. She would not hide behind smoked lenses. 'Weren't you?'

Laura shrugged. 'I don't suppose I worked as hard as you did,' she remarked, and Catherine was disconcerted.

'No?'

'At organising the party.' Laura's explanation came as a disappointment; Catherine hated verbal fencing with other women. 'I expect you and Elizabeth helped one another.'

Catherine sighed and sank down into the cushions of a chair nearby. 'Why don't you say it, Laura?' she asked impatiently. 'Why don't you come right out and tell me what you really mean?'

Laura licked her lips, straightened her spine, and held her knees tightly together. 'I don't know what you mean.'

'Yes, you do.' Catherine leaned towards her. 'Why don't you tell me to lay off Jared? That's why you're here, isn't it?'

'*No!*' Laura was obviously horrified. She got abruptly to her feet, staring at Catherine in dismay. 'I—I came to see whether you would care to lunch at Fourwinds, that's all. Why should I want to cause a scene?' She squared her shoulders. 'If you're worried about dancing with Jared last evening, I think you're exaggerating its significance. Jared dances with lots of other girls, and besides, he explained how Johnny wanted to change partners. I'm not jealous! Don't be silly!'

Catherine rested her head back against the latticed upholstery. She had to accept what Laura was saying. What else could she do? Whatever her feelings, Laura was not about to unburden herself to a virtual stranger.

'Fourwinds?' she said now, questioningly.

'My home.' Laura linked her fingers together. 'As Jared isn't here, and Elizabeth is busy, I thought you might enjoy an outing.'

Catherine got reluctantly to her feet and paced over to stare down into the clear waters of the pool. The last thing she wanted was to spend the day in Laura's company, but if she refused and it got back to the servants, it would only give more room for gossip in the kitchen.

'Where is Jared?' she inquired, despising herself for doing so.

Laura adjusted the cushions on the lounger where she had been sitting. 'Down at the beach house, I understand.'

Catherine swung round. 'Flintlock?'

Laura nodded, straightening. 'Have you been there?'

'Once.' Catherine turned her back again.

'I don't expect we shall see him for a few days,' Laura commented, her casual words bringing a tightening to the nerves throughout Catherine's body.

'No?'

'No.' Laura picked up her handbag. 'Henry told me he loaded the car with his equipment first thing. We all know what that means.'

Catherine turned again. 'What does it mean?'

'It means he's finding it impossible to work in the house. After all, he does have this commission to finish for the legislative building.'

There were pockets in Catherine's dress, and she pushed her hands into them. 'What commission?'

'A portrait of the governor-general's wife,' said Laura proudly.

'But . . .' Catherine looked bemused. 'Has she been here? I haven't seen her.'

'Oh, no.' Laura shook her head quite scornfully now. 'Jared works from sketches mostly. All painters have their own particular style, and Jared finds he works best without human distraction.'

'Does he?' Catherine was impressed in spite of herself.

'Yes. Haven't you noticed that portrait of his mother in the dining room? Jared did that. After she was dead, of course. He was very young when she died.'

Catherine remembered the portrait very well. She had admired it on a number of occasions since she had first noticed it. 'He's very clever,' she said rather flatly, and Laura nodded, her expression quite smug.

'Yes, he is, isn't he?' Her fingers moulded the wood back of the chair. 'You've no idea how marvellous it is being engaged to someone like that.' She held out her left hand, so that Catherine could admire the solitaire diamond on her finger. 'Jared used to be so—well, I believe he had quite a reputation when he was younger. But since we got together . . .' She smiled, but Catherine had turned away, hating herself for the emotions she was experiencing. Laura wasn't deliberately boasting of her achievement. It just sounded that way.

'Well?' Laura was speaking again. 'How about it? Lunch with my parents? You will come, won't you, Catherine? I know they'd love to have you.'

Catherine thought of having lunch alone with Elizabeth and came to a reluctant decision. 'All right.' She managed to smile. 'I'll come. If you're sure that's what you want to do.'

'Marvellous!' Laura was so enthusiastic, she made Catherine feel even worse. 'Let's go, then, shall we? You can leave a message for Elizabeth with one of the servants. I'm sure she won't mind.'

Catherine didn't care for being hurried, but she had accepted Laura's invitation now, and there was nothing she could do to change that, even if she had wanted to. Susie was dusting the stairs when she went into the hall, and she left word with her that she and Miss Prentiss were lunching out. At least that way she could be sure that the news would reach every member of the household, she thought dryly.

Fourwinds was a sprawling, split-level dwelling, built on an incline above a small lake. Long windows stood wide to the scents from the gardens that were terraced down to the lakeside, where a dinghy with an outboard motor rocked against a stone jetty. Behind the house were canefields, and as they drove up the narrow drive, overhung with shrubs and palms and thickly flowering thorn bushes, Laura explained that although her father had retired now, he employed an estates manager to run the small plantation for him. Catherine could see a windmill in the middle of the grey-plumed stalks, its sails turning slowly in the breeze, no doubt pumping water from the lake into the fields. Two dark-skinned Bajuns were at work in the gardens, but they stopped and leaned on their spades as the two girls drove by. The whole atmosphere was one of unhurried indolence.

Mr Prentiss was sitting on the verandah at the front of the house, which overlooked the terraced gardens and the blue-shadowed waters of the lake beyond. He looked up as Laura brought her sports car to a halt at the side of the building, and came to meet them as they walked up the slope towards him. He was a man in his late fifties, Catherine supposed, and although she had met him twice before, she had not held a conversation with him. Of medium height and slightly built, greying hair and sun-lined features, he was a quiet man, usually content to allow his wife and daughter to speak for him.

But now he held out his hand to Catherine and his smile was warm and genuine. 'Welcome to Fourwinds,' he said, admiring the picture she made in her green dress, her hair dry now and escaping in honey-gold strands from the ribbon. 'Come and have a cool drink before lunch.'

'Thank you.' Catherine found it easy to smile now. 'What an attractive view you have!'

Mr Prentiss exchanged a look of acknowledgement with his daughter. 'Yes, we do. As we can't see the sea from our windows, we have the next best thing.'

'Do you swim in the lake?'

Laura laughed. 'Well, Daddy doesn't. But I do—sometimes.'

'That's as close to the water as I get these days,' said her father, indicating the dinghy. 'Do you sail, Catherine?'

'I've never tried, I'm afraid. It wasn't one of my father's passions, and I guess I've never got round to it.'

They mounted the steps to the verandah, and as they did so, Laura's mother came through the french doors to join them. She was a plumper edition of Laura, her dark hair showing few grey strands, although her skin belied her real age. She greeted Catherine with only slightly less warmth than her husband, and they all made themselves comfortable in the cushioned rattan chairs. Catherine had her first taste of iced punch, a mixture of lime juice and sugar, with just a dash of angostura, liberally laced with rum. It was delicious, and she felt herself relaxing and occasionally joining in the undemanding conversation. Mrs Prentiss's penchant for talking made everybody else's contribution less important, and it was pleasant just to drowse there in the sun, watching the bees among the flowers, hearing the gentle lap of water against the reeds bordering the lake.

Lunch was served in a white-walled dining room, with an enormous fan stirring the air above their heads. Shellfish salad, and a fruit mousse, were exactly what one needed on such a hot day, and afterwards, Mrs Prentiss suggested that Catherine might like to look over the house.

Catherine would have preferred to return to the shade of the verandah. The punch had been stronger than she had imagined, and that, combined with the wine she had consumed during lunch, had served to make her feel pleasantly lethargic. But Laura and her mother shared the same eager enthusiasm which made it difficult to refuse. She had expected Laura would accompany them, but she went to join her father leaving Catherine to Mrs Prentiss's mercies.

Fourwinds was more modern than Amaryllis, the furnishings similar to what Catherine had been used to in London. She tried to show a genuine interest in what her hostess was saying, but looking round other people's houses had never been a fetish with her. Nevertheless, it soon became apparent that showing Catherine the house had had secondary motivations. Before long, Mrs Prentiss brought the conversation round to the Royals, and waiting for the denunciation which she was sure was to come, Catherine was startled when Laura's mother began to speak about Elizabeth.

'How do you—er—get on with Jared's stepmother?' she asked, casually.

Catherine shrugged. How to answer that? 'I—we don't see a lot of one another,' she replied evasively. 'You know she spends a lot of time down at the stables, I suppose?'

'Yes.' Mrs Prentiss opened the door into a low, light lounge. 'This is our sitting room,' she said, rather absently, then: 'Has she discussed with you what she's going to do when Laura and Jared get married?'

'No.' Catherine ran her fingers over the smooth hide of a low couch. 'I love this tan-coloured leather——'

'Did you realise there was gossip about her and Jared just after his father died?'

Catherine half turned away, faint colour invading her cheeks. 'People always gossip,' she answered lightly.

'I know. And I don't honestly believe there was anything in it,' Mrs Prentiss hastened on. 'Not on Jared's side, at least. But—well, Elizabeth Royal was always aware of her stepson. Anyone could see that. Some said she only took the old man when it became obvious she was getting nowhere with the son. And when James died——'

'Really, Mrs Prentiss, I don't see what this has to do with me.' Catherine's nails dug into the soft leather. 'Surely if you have any doubts about Jared's relationship with his stepmother, you should take them up with him.'

Mrs Prentiss sniffed. 'As if I could do that!' she exclaimed resentfully. 'Don't you know, Jared won't have a word said against the woman? But he and Laura have been engaged for almost two years. It's time they were thinking of getting married. But so far as I know, no definite arrangements have even been discussed!'

Catherine felt an unpleasant stirring of emotion inside

her. 'It's really nothing to do with me, Mrs Prentiss,' she repeated faintly, wondering what the woman would say if she knew how she was feeling right at this moment, remembering that less than twelve hours ago she had been in Jared's arms ...

'But you live in the house, Catherine,' Laura's mother was persisting. 'And Laura told us how you spoke up to Jared in her defence last week. Oh'—she shook her head, —'she didn't describe it to me in quite those terms. She's a fool where he's concerned. But I realised what you were trying to do for her.'

'Mrs Prentiss——'

'No. Let me finish.' The older woman held up her hand. 'I hoped I might persuade you to—speak to Elizabeth. Casually, you understand. Sort of—sound her out about— well, about the situation.'

'Oh, but I——'

'Laura won't push herself, you see,' exclaimed Mrs Prentiss, pressing her balled fists together. 'She won't ask questions. She's quite content to sit back and let the Royals walk all over her. Well, I won't let her. Someone has to do something. This engagement could drag on indefinitely.'

Catherine took a deep breath. It crossed her mind, rather uncharitably perhaps, that by attempting to enlist her aid, Mrs Prentiss was hoping to dispose of any threat she might present. But whatever her motives, there was nothing she could do.

'Why don't you speak to Elizabeth?' Catherine asked now, wishing either Laura or her father would appear to interrupt them. 'Surely you could mention it to her.'

Mrs Prentiss's nostrils flared angrily. 'Do you think I haven't? Elizabeth Royal is a past mistress in the art of sophistry! There's always something in the way of a direct answer—something she's arranged, some bloodstock sale she has to attend, some commission Jared has to finish . . .'

'Well,' Catherine snatched at a passing straw, 'as a matter of fact, Jared's working on a commission right now.'

'The portrait for the Legislature, yes, I know.' Mrs Prentiss made an impatient gesture. 'But that must surely be almost completed.'

'I understand he left this morning——'

'*Left?*'

'For the beach house.' Catherine shifted uncomfortably. 'Laura told me, actually.'

'He's left for the beach house? To finish this commission, one supposes?'

'I believe so.'

Mrs Prentiss sighed angrily. 'Isn't that just like a man? Running away from his responsibilities?'

Catherine cleared her throat. 'His—responsibilities?' she echoed.

'Of course.' The older woman stared at her. 'You, Catherine, you! He invites you here, into his home, and then abandons you.'

'I'm not a child, Mrs Prentiss.'

'I know that. Even so, he knows—at least, he must know —how much Laura wants to get married, and yet he persists in behaving in this irresponsible fashion! I suppose it's the artistic temperament. I suppose we must make some allowances for that. But I do think he takes a shameful advantage of Laura. She's a lovely girl. There are several young men who would envy him his good fortune in being her fiancé. But what does he do? He treats her with no respect whatsoever!'

Catherine made an effort to escape. 'I—don't you think we ought to be joining the others?' she suggested hopefully, but Laura's mother wasn't quite finished.

'If Jared is away,' she was musing slowly, 'what a wonderful opportunity you'll have for talking to Elizabeth.'

'But——'

Mrs Prentiss made a soothing gesture. 'Please. I'm not asking you to be indiscreet. Just to—well, discuss the wedding. A casual word here and there. You could learn so much.'

'I doubt it.'

'Oh, I knew I could rely on you!'

Mrs Prentiss took her dry comment as acceptance, and before Catherine had time to protest, she had turned and crossed the hall, calling for one of the servants to bring afternoon tea to them on the verandah. It was deliberately done, Catherine knew that, but she could say nothing. And besides, what had Laura's mother gained after all? She could not be compelled to relay her conversations with Elizabeth back to the Prentisses . . . could she?

Driving Catherine back to Amaryllis, Laura was much more relaxed. 'You and Mummy get on incredibly well, don't you?' she enthused, giving her companion a sidelong glance. 'I'm so glad. She doesn't always like my friends.'

Catherine let this go without comment. She was feeling raw and vulnerable, and out of sorts with herself. What was it about these people that made her feel so sensitive? Why did they persist in involving her in their schemes? She and Laura were not really friends at all. They were acquaintances, that was all. And she did not get on well with Laura's mother. On the contrary, she felt a strong aversion towards her. All she was, was a stranger, a guest in the Royal house, not even a distant relative. She knew nothing about them or their plans, and she didn't want to know. If Mrs Prentiss wanted her daughter married, she should say so to the only person who could do anything about it. Jared! And why didn't he marry her, anyway? If they had been engaged so long, what were they waiting for? Money was no obstacle, on either side. The Royal house was big enough to accommodate half a dozen families. So why the delay? Was Elizabeth the obstruction? Or was Jared reluctant to make the final commitment? Oh, *God*! Catherine could feel tears smarting behind her eyes. It was nothing to do with her. Why couldn't they accept that? Why couldn't *she* accept it?

Laura refused her invitation to come in when they arrived back at Amaryllis. 'I'd better gèt home,' she said, slipping the car into bottom gear. 'Thanks all the same. I'll probably see you tomorrow. We might go to Sam Lord's Castle. Would you like that? We could have lunch there. I'm sure you'd like to see it.'

Catherine could think of no good reason for refusing, but she needed some time to herself. 'Make it the day after tomorrow,' she said, and then despised herself when Laura's anticipatory smile disappeared.

'The day after tomorrow?' she said, with evident disappointment. 'Oh! Well—all right. But what are you going to do tomorrow?'

Catherine gripped her handbag very tightly, forcing a casual tone. 'Just have a lazy day,' she answered. 'See you!'

'See you,' echoed Laura, with a sigh, and Catherine entered the house feeling an absolute pig.

Lily was waiting for her in the hall.

'Miz Royal wants to see you, Miz Fulton,' she said, rather diffidently. 'She's in the library. Will you go straight through?'

Catherine sighed now. After her conversation with Mrs Prentiss, the last thing she needed was a scene with Elizabeth.

'I—will you tell Mrs Royal I'm just going up to wash my hands,' she said, going towards the stairs, but as Lily nodded her head and turned away, Elizabeth's voice arrested her:

'Have you a minute, Catherine?'

Catherine turned, one hand resting on the baluster. 'I was just going to rinse my face and hands, Mrs Royal,' she explained tightly.

'I'm sure that can wait,' replied Elizabeth imperiously. 'If you don't mind . . .'

Catherine saw the sympathetic look in Lily's eyes as she made her way back to the kitchens, and took strength from it. Holding her head high, she preceded Elizabeth into the library.

Elizabeth was still wearing her working attire of silk shirt and jodhpurs, which was strange for this hour of the afternoon. But perhaps as Jared wasn't here, she had less interest in her appearance, thought Catherine, realising as she did so that she had never felt her felinity so strongly as she did with this woman.

'You've been to Fourwinds,' Elizabeth said, as she closed the library doors.

'Yes.' Catherine saw no reason to enlarge upon it.

'Laura invited you.'

'Of course.'

'Of course.' Elizabeth indicated a chair, but Catherine preferred to stand. 'It's reassuring to know she thinks of you as a friend.'

Catherine let that go. 'You wanted to speak to me, Mrs Royal?' she prompted.

Elizabeth sighed, subsiding into a low chair with her usual grace. 'Oh, dear, we've come a long way in ten days, haven't we? We began as friends, and what are we now? Antagonists —enemies?'

'I think you're exaggerating, Mrs Royal.'

'I hope so. I really hope so.' She bit her lip delicately. 'About last night, Catherine——'

'I really don't think we——'

'Please! Don't jump to conclusions. I was about to apologise for—for perhaps making more of something that everyone else sees in its true perspective. I'm sorry. There—now will you sit down?'

Catherine felt an immense sense of weariness enveloping her. 'Why did you want to speak to me, Mrs Royal?'

Elizabeth exhibited a moment's impatience. 'I'm trying to tell you, Catherine,' she snapped. Then she forced a smile. 'You could help by telling me that you accept my apology.'

Catherine bent her head. She knew she was being ungracious, but she couldn't help it. She was so tired. 'It doesn't matter,' she said quietly. 'And I'm sorry you felt the need to say anything.' She looked up. 'If that's all . . .'

'It's not all.' Elizabeth pressed her lips together for a moment. 'I—I wanted to talk to you about—the wedding.'

'The *wedding*?' Twice in one afternoon? It was too much! Catherine stared at her bewilderedly. 'What wedding?'

'*The* wedding. Our wedding. Jared and Laura's wedding, of course.' Elizabeth linked her fingers together. 'You must have known they were planning to get married. People don't get engaged for nothing, now do they?'

'I—I——' Catherine could feel her mouth opening and shutting like a fish and endeavoured to prevent it. 'I—didn't realise anything was arranged.'

'No? Well, you haven't been here long enough to know everything, have you?' inquired Elizabeth pleasantly. 'However, it's been understood for some time that the engagement has lasted long enough. Naturally Jared didn't want to rush things after his father died, but I think a suitable interval has elapsed now, don't you? It crossed my mind that you might be glad of the diversion. You can't find life too exciting here. Not after London. And who knows, once he's married, perhaps Jared will allow you to return to England,

105

and the—friends you have there.'

There was a coldness flooding Catherine's system. It began in her stomach, a hard little core of ice, that spread its chilling tentacles to the extremities of her being. So that was it, she thought bitterly. For some reason, Elizabeth had decided she wanted her out of the house, and if it meant submitting to Jared's marriage to Laura, she was prepared to do it. She must have known that sooner or later the situation would arise, so why not now? Mrs Prentiss, at least, would be delighted!

'This is rather sudden, isn't it?' Catherine couldn't quite keep the edge out of her voice. 'Laura didn't mention it to me, and I'm sure she would have done if ...'

Elizabeth took a moment to smooth the cloth of her breeches. 'As a matter of fact, Jared and I only discussed it last night. After you had gone to bed.'

'But you cou——' Catherine broke off, biting her tongue. She had almost fallen into the trap Elizabeth had unwittingly laid for her. Or was it unwitting? She couldn't be absolutely sure Elizabeth didn't know about that late night outing. Jared might well have told her. Catherine's flesh crept at the thought. Shaking her head, she muttered: 'It was—rather late, wasn't it?'

'Jared told me he intended spending a few days at the beach house. I thought we should get matters settled before he left.'

Catherine looked into Elizabeth's complacent face, and wished she knew the truth. Had Jared spoken to his stepmother after he got back in the early hours of the morning? How could he have done so? Unless their relationship overstepped the bounds of common decency ... She shivered, in spite of the heat of the day. She couldn't believe that he could have come back to Elizabeth after making such violent love to her. But if he hadn't, was all this a lie?

106

A fabrication? Would Elizabeth dare to suggest such a thing without Jared's permission? Catherine had to concede that she probably would not.

'So,' she shifted restlessly, 'when is the wedding to be?' She would not let Elizabeth see how much this news had shocked her.

'These things take a little time to arrange,' replied Elizabeth, crossing her legs. 'Six or eight weeks, I should think.'

'Eight weeks.' Catherine's lips tightened. 'Laura will be pleased.'

Elizabeth met her gaze without flinching. 'I'm sure we all are,' she countered silkily, and Catherine had the strongest urge to scratch her eyes out.

CHAPTER SEVEN

CATHERINE had a letter from Tony next morning. It was like a breath of fresh air to read his jaunty writing, reminding her that despite his difficulties, he had never buckled under the strain.

She had written to him just over a week ago, giving him her address, and a brief but amusing résumé of events since her arrival. She had touched a little on the antagonism Jared was exhibiting towards her, but had omitted to mention the deception she was practising. She guessed that Tony would not approve of that, whatever her newly-appointed guardian might think of him.

Elizabeth came into the morning room as Catherine was finishing her breakfast, and her eyes immediately alighted on the letter with its British postmark.

'The boy-friend, one presumes,' she commented slyly, and Catherine snatched up the letter and thrust it into the pocket of her jeans.

'A friend, yes,' she conceded shortly.

Elizabeth smiled, and Catherine suddenly realised she was not wearing her working clothes. Instead, she was slim and elegant in a lime green skirt suit, the green and white striped lapels of the jacket matching the contrasting hem of the skirt. It was the first time Catherine had seen her legs without covering, but although they were quite short, they were as neatly proportioned as the rest of her.

'I expect you're wondering where I'm going,' Elizabeth remarked, noting the girl's admiring interest with mild satisfaction. 'As a matter of fact, I rang Marion Prentiss. I thought we should get together—to discuss the arrangements and so on. She was most agreeable, so I'm going over there this morning. I suggested that you might like to come along too, but she said that you had told Laura that you wanted a lazy day. Is that right? I must say, you did look rather—peaky, yesterday evening. Perhaps our climate doesn't agree with you, after all.'

There was a grain of maliciousness in what Elizabeth was saying, although it was delivered with a conciliatory smile. Catherine chose to accept it in kind.

'On the contrary,' she said smoothly, 'I love this weather, and I'm never happier than when I'm sunbathing. If I looked a little tired, it's because Laura is so—energetic. Too energetic for me, I'm afraid.'

Elizabeth's smile disappeared. 'So you don't want to come?'

'No, thanks.' Catherine finished her coffee and pushed the empty cup aside. 'But don't worry about me. I don't get bored. I'm very happy here.'

Elizabeth drove away soon after ten, and Catherine breathed a sigh of relief when the sound of the engine died away. With Jared at the beach house, she had the house to herself, and there was a certain excitement in the thought. All those rooms that she had never explored. Elizabeth was not like Mrs Prentiss. She had not taken her guest on a conducted tour. But then perhaps Mrs Prentiss wouldn't have done if she hadn't wanted something. How astonished she must have been to receive Elizabeth's call. Catherine couldn't help a small smile. Did Laura's mother think she had had anything to do with it? Well, in a way, she supposed she had, she mused. But not in the way Marion Prentiss would think.

Leaving the lounger beside the pool, she strolled restlessly through the gardens. Henry's brother, Raoul, was trimming the hedges beside the path that flanked the tennis courts, and his big brown eyes widened at the sight of her in scanty red shorts and a white halter top. Flushing, Catherine beat a hasty retreat, walking back to the edge of the pool and staring down frowningly into its depths.

She wondered what Jared was doing. Was he working? Was he finding it easier to concentrate down at the beach house, within sight and sound of the surf he loved, than in the isolated confines of his studio? His studio ...

Turning, her eyes sought the second floor of the house. It was up there somewhere. She knew it was. She had once questioned Susie when she encountered the girl carrying a tray of food upstairs. There was a second staircase, at the end of the corridor opposite to the one where her room was situated. But no one went up there. Except by invitation ...

With assumed nonchalance, she walked into the house. Lily was in the morning room, clearing away the breakfast dishes, and she looked expectantly at her.

'You want something, Miz Fulton?' she asked, straightening from her task.

'I—no, nothing, thank you, Lily,' Catherine gave her a faint smile. 'I'm—just going up to my room, for—for a book.'

Lily nodded and resumed what she was doing while Catherine walked quickly across the room and ran lightly up the stairs. But on the gallery, she paused. Did she really intend invading his studio? Dared she do such a thing? And what if she was discovered?

She sighed impatiently, angry with her own indecisiveness. No one knew she did not have permission to enter the studio, and she intended no harm, after all. She just wanted to see where he worked, to examine some of his canvases.

She walked along the corridor she had seen Susie taking

110

with the tray with an outward confidence it was hard to simulate. But if she was seen, it would be better to look as if she knew where she was going.

She reached the end of the corridor without incident and there it was—the narrower flight of stairs leading to the second floor. Taking a deep breath, she lifted her foot on to the first step, and dismissing the twinges of her conscience climbed to the top.

She was on a narrow landing with only two doors opening from it. Which to choose? She bit her lip and turned the handle of the first. It was a bathroom, and she closed the door again quickly, and reached for the second.

She found herself looking into an enormous apartment which seemed to stretch across half the width of the house. Long windows on three sides could let in the maximum amount of daylight, but right now shafts of sunlight only filtered through the slatted blinds. As in the beach house, the walls were stacked with canvases, but there were also drawing boards, tables bright with jars and tubes of colour, oils and enamels, varnishes, bottles containing brushes, pens and charcoal, palette knives, pads and drawing tablets, all the paraphernalia associated with the craft. It was a veritable Aladdin's cave, and Catherine closed the door and leaned back against it, savouring the delights of exploration.

An easel stood in the middle of the floor, bare of any canvas. She guessed Jared had taken whatever had been on it with him. The portrait of the governor-general's lady, perhaps. The commission which was demanding his undivided attention.

She sighed and straightened, walking across the floor boards lightly, unwilling to alert anyone downstairs to an awareness of her whereabouts. She guessed this room had been specially designed to meet Jared's needs, but she doubted it was soundproofed.

There was a door at the far side of the room, and it opened, as she half expected, into a second corridor with more doors opening from it. Probably at one time, this top floor of the building had had similar proportions to the lower floors, but the need to expand the studio had divided the house. She wondered why the studio had not been built at this side of the house, but as she retraced her steps, her question answered itself. The windows at the side of the studio commanded a magnificent view of the distant ocean.

She walked across the room again, bending to examine some of the canvases leaning against the walls. They covered an amazing variety of subjects—some portraits, some landscapes—figures imprisoned forever in scenes alive with passion and colour. The workers in the cane fields, scythes catching the sunlight, faces dark and alert, teeth white and realistically uneven. The yachts down at the Careenage, the harbour policemen in their uniforms, the shellfish squirming in their pots. There were fishermen and sailors, market vendors with their goods, the wobbling wheels of the 'Jackass' carts had a dimension Catherine had seldom seen. Windmills and ruined plantation houses, the sails of a schooner in the sunset, and the seething, rolling thunder of the surf.

She was enthralled, entranced, fascinated by a talent so tangible she could actually feel it. On her knees, she turned over the canvases, feeling no sense of intrusion, absorbed as in an exhibition that had to be shared.

Behind the canvases, she came upon a handful of sketches, swiftly executed things of charcoal, pushed away where no one might be expected to see them. She turned them over rapidly, eyes widening in disbelief as she recognised their subject. Her own face stared back at her in a dozen different moods, sad and wistful, alert and excited, sulky or just plain provocative. But not just her face—her body as well, unclothed, and burgeoning with motherhood.

Her lips parted on a gasp, half admiration, half dismay, and as she sat there with the sketches in her hands, she heard footsteps on the stairs, and a moment later the studio door was thrust open. She had expected it might be Susie, Henry even, or at the outside, Elizabeth. But Jared stood there staring at her, and her hands trembled uncontrollably at the look in his eyes.

'What are you doing?' he demanded, striding across the floor and snatching the sketches out of her grasp. 'Who gave you permission to come up here? Where's Liz? I don't believe she would do such a thing?'

Catherine remained on her knees. She had not seen Jared since she had ridden away on his motor-bike leaving him stranded at the beach, and the enormity of both offences momentarily paralysed her. He looked down at her angrily, tall and disturbingly masculine in a denim waistcoat and jeans, the rolled up sketches beating a tattoo against his thigh.

'Well?' he said. 'Are you dumb as well as deaf? What are you doing up here?'

Catherine expelled her breath on a sigh. 'I should have thought that was obvious. I wanted to see where you worked. I was curious. Is that unreasonable?'

'You should have asked me if you wanted to come up here.'

'Oh, yes?' She looked up at him bitterly. 'And I suppose you'd have granted my request?' She bent her head again. 'Well, anyway, it's done now. I'm sorry if you object.'

'Are you?' The sketches were thrust aside, and he hauled her unceremoniously to her feet. 'Don't pay lip service to me, Catherine! I know you too well. You're not

113

sorry—except perhaps that you were caught!' His hands were heavy at her armpits. 'Well, I hope you're satisfied now!'

She looked up into his lean dark face, and fear had no part of the emotions she was experiencing now. She was remembering what had happened between them before she leapt on to his motor-cycle and rode away—remembering his unleashed passion, the same passion she had just admired in his paintings, in those sketches that mocked the savagery of his anger.

'Are you?' she breathed huskily, and felt his fingers tightening as they moved down the sides of her body to her waist and lower ... He was looking down at her, heavy lids shadowing the grim frustration in his eyes, his mouth twisting as he acknowledged her awareness of his weakness. 'You're supposed to be at the beach house,' she whispered, her tongue appearing to moisten her upper lip, and he nodded his head in bleak resignation.

'I know, I know. But I had to come back. There were things I needed ...' A pulse beat rapidly near his hairline, and his jaw was clenched tight.

'Wh—what things?' she probed, stretching out a hand to explore the hollow of his navel, but he knocked her fingers away and with a supreme effort thrust her away from him.

'Get out of here!' he commanded violently. 'Before I deliver the beating you deserve!'

Catherine began to tremble again, but she refused to let him see how he had hurt her. 'What are you going to do with those sketches?' she asked quietly, and he swung round to face her.

'These?' He picked up the sketches from the table nearby where he had tossed them minutes before. His expression was cold and sardonic. 'What am I going to do with these? Why, what I always do with things that don't please me: I destroy them!' And before she realised his intention, he had torn the charcoal drawings into shreds and thrown the pieces into the waste bin.

Catherine was appalled. They had been so brilliant, so *alive*, so much a part of her that his destruction of them seemed like a partial destruction of herself.

'You—you *swine*!' she choked, staring down into the bin, seeing the scattered scraps of paper like some fantastic jigsaw puzzle that could never be solved.

'Now perhaps you'll keep away from me,' he snarled. 'You have to live in my house—but that's enough!'

Catherine stared at him blankly. 'You don't honestly think it's as easy as that!'

'Don't I?'

'You drew those sketches.'

'Yes, I did. And you know why.'

'Pagan motherhood? Oh, yes, I remember. But I never posed for you. Does Laura know about this?'

'Keep Laura's name out of it!'

'Why should I? She's so proud of you.' Catherine's voice broke on the words, but pride and something else, something she did not want to acknowledge, was driving her on. 'I'd have thought she would be the first to compliment you on the vividness of your imagina——'

'Shut up!'

With a tormented groan, he reached for her, his hands sliding round her neck, his thumbs closing on the veins throbbing beneath his fingers.

'I could kill you,' he muttered bitterly, 'I could squeeze the life out of you and dispose of your body without anyone being any the wiser!'

'Could you?'

It was less than a whisper and he breathed a defeated

sigh. 'No. *No!*' He shuddered as he impelled her towards him, his hands sliding over her shoulders and down her arms, finding her hands and gripping them tightly. 'Oh, Catherine—*Catherine!*'

He spoke her name against her mouth, his breath filling her throat, parting her lips with his tongue and caressing them with his own. His eyes were open, looking into hers, but when she moved against him, she saw the darkening emotion narrowing their tawny penetration. His hands closed on the tops of her thighs and she felt the iron hardness of his body. She lifted her arms to his waist, hooking her thumbs into the low waistband of his jeans, pressing herself closer.

He seemed to have been holding himself in check, but the yielding softness of her body against his own released the need inside him. His mouth hardened into passion, possessing hers with a rousing urgency that left her weak and clinging to him.

'This is madness!' he protested against her hair, but she shivered convulsively beneath his questing hands. 'Dear God—kiss me! Again! Catherine, you do know what I'm going to do to you, don't you? Oh, God, of course you do . . .'

'Stop tormenting yourself, Jared,' she breathed into his chest. 'You don't understand.'

'I don't want to——'

'Jared! Jared, are you up there? Is Catherine with you?'

'*Laura!*'

Jared's hoarse ejaculation was only audible to the girl in his arms. Laura's voice echoed clearly up the narrow stairway, and Catherine's legs refused to continue to support her. When Jared dragged himself away from her, she sank down weakly on to the floorboards, crosslegged, shoulders drooping, her head almost touching her knees.

Jared cast one desperate look in her direction and then raking his hands through his hair, he walked to the head of the staircase. If his voice was a little uneven as he answered his fiancée, only Catherine was sensitive enough to hear it. She heard Laura's footsteps as she mounted the stairs, and then determinedly lifted her head as the other girl entered the studio.

'Oh, you are here, Catherine,' she exclaimed lightly, and once more Catherine was astounded by her capacity to turn a blind eye to anything that didn't appeal to her. Didn't she really suspect what had been going on? Couldn't she tell from Catherine's bruised mouth what Jared had been doing to her? Hadn't she glimpsed the slightly glazed look in Jared's eyes?

Apparently not. Laura tucked her hand through her fiancé's arm, looking up at him adoringly. 'I came over to see Catherine, actually. I was so excited about the news, and I had to share it with somebody. But when Lily told me that you were here . . .' She reached up and kissed his cheek. 'Oh, darling, thank you!'

Jared looked as if he could use a drink, and disentangling himself from her clinging hands, he walked across the room to stare grimly out of the window.

'Don't thank me, Laura,' he told her bleakly. 'It was Liz's idea. I'm not sure it was a good one.'

So they had discussed it!

Catherine scrambled to her feet. She had no part of this conversation, and again she was seeing Laura's air of confidence disintegrate.

'I'll—go down——' she began awkwardly, but Jared turned to stare at her, supporting himself with his hands against the sill.

'Why?' he demanded. 'Don't you want to hear my reasons?'

117

'Jared——' She glanced helplessly at Laura.

'What's wrong?' He seemed bent on a course of self-destruction. 'Laura knows what's been going on, don't you, Laura? She just doesn't want to acknowledge it.'

'*Jared!*'

Catherine's cheeks flamed, but Laura had, if anything, lost colour. She stood there listening to what Jared was saying, and although her expression had hardly altered, she looked frozen.

Catherine shuddered. This was awful! What was Jared trying to do? How could he profess to love someone and then treat them so abominably? Didn't he care what Laura was feeling?

'Isn't that right, Laura?'

Jared seemed determined that she should answer him, and she moved her shoulders in a helpless little gesture. 'I shouldn't have come here,' she said tremulously. 'I realise that now. You're still upset because you haven't finished the commission——'

'Damn the commission!' he swore angrily. 'Don't you listen to anything I say? I've been kissing Catherine, Laura, do you hear me? I've been holding her in my arms and caressing her, and if you hadn't interrupted us, I'd have made love to her——'

'*No!*'

Now it was Catherine who interrupted him, and he turned to glare at her furiously. 'What do you mean? No?'

'I mean—no. I—I wouldn't have let you.'

'You couldn't have stopped me!' His lips twisted mockingly. 'You forget—I know you, Catherine. I know *all* about you. And there's something about once having tasted the fruits——'

Catherine's fingers stung across his cheek, and her hand tingled long after the tell-tale marks had appeared on his

118

dark skin. She slapped him for herself—and for Laura; and for all the agony he evoked inside her ...

For a moment she thought he intended to return the slap. His hand moved—but went to his face, his fingers probing the marks hers had made. Laura uttered a sob of dismay, and then she interposed herself between them, pushing Jared's hand aside and examining his face with anxious eyes.

'Oh, darling,' she exclaimed, her voice breaking, 'this is all my fault! Say you forgive me. I can't bear it when you're cruel to me!'

As Catherine turned unsteadily away, she encountered Jared's hard gaze above Laura's head. The contempt she read there filled her with despair, and she groped her way towards the door. She didn't understand this—she didn't understand *them*. What did it all mean? Would Laura really accept Jared on *any* terms?

On the first floor, she made her way almost automatically to her own room. She felt sick, physically nauseated by the scene she had just witnessed, torn to pieces by emotions she did not want to identify. Could Laura intend marrying Jared knowing that he was already unfaithful to her, in mind if not in body? Had she no pride? No self-respect? No pain at her own humiliation? So long as she wore his ring, was that all she cared about?

And why had Jared created that terrible scene anyway? Why couldn't he have allowed her to remain ignorant of what had occurred, even if it was only feigned? What had he hoped to gain by his revelations?

Catherine realised she was trembling, and sat down jerkily on the side of her bed. Oh, God, she thought shakily, why couldn't she hate him? Why couldn't she despise him? Was she no better than Laura? Would she be prepared to accept him on his terms?

119

She got up again and paced about her bedroom. No, she told herself fiercely, *no*! She pitied Laura, that was all. She pitied any woman who was so obsessed with a man that she would go to any lengths to keep him. And there was still Elizabeth ...

Elizabeth—with whom he had discussed his wedding to Laura. But when? When he got back in the early hours that morning? Had he gone to her room? Had he confided what had happened to her? Had *she* soothed and comforted him?

Bile rose in the back of Catherine's throat, and she struggled to reach the bathroom, leaning over the basin until the violent spasm passed. But not everything passed so simply, she thought, grasping the door frame to support herself, as the room swam dizzily around her.

Her hands were hot and sticky with sweat, slippery against the smooth wood. She couldn't hold on. She could feel herself sliding down through waves of giddiness, but she could do nothing to save herself ...

CHAPTER EIGHT

CATHERINE recovered consciousness as someone was lifting her on to the bed. She opened her eyes slowly, and blinked incredulously up into Jared's dark angry face.

'Wh—what happened?'

'You passed out,' he replied grimly, lowering her on to the pillows, slipping off her sandals and dropping them on the floor at his feet. 'How do you feel now?'

'I'm'— Catherine glimpsed Laura's anxious face hovering behind him, and it all came flooding back, 'I'm all right.'

'Are you?' He seemed curiously unconvinced.

'What are you doing here?' she protested, trying to prop herself up on her elbows, but finding the effort too much for her.

Jared glanced over his shoulder at Laura, and a strange expression crossed his face. 'I was—concerned about you,' he muttered half angrily. He stared down at her. 'Do you need a doctor?'

She realised what he meant, and the ridiculousness of it all brought tears of frustration to her eyes. She moved her head slowly from side to side, feeling the dampness on her cheeks.

'Oh, *God*, Catherine!' Jared cast another grim look in Laura's direction. 'You know what I mean.'

'Yes, I know what you mean,' she mumbled, 'but no! I don't need anything.'

Jared expelled his breath on an angry sigh. 'All right, all right! We'll leave you.' He indicated that Laura should precede him to the door. 'I'll get Susie to fetch you some aspirin.'

'It's probably the heat,' remarked Laura complacently, and Catherine was amazed at her lack of perception. Or was it a lack? She could never be sure now.

'The *heat*!' Jared's harsh echo of her words was barely audible. 'You're sure you'll be all right?'

'I've said so!' Catherine nodded jerkily, just wanting to be alone.

'I think you should tell Elizabeth,' he added, and they both knew to what he was referring.

'There's nothing to tell!' she retorted tearfully, and turned her face into the pillow. Let him make what he liked of that!

She must have slept because when she opened her eyes, Susie was sitting beside the bed, idly folding pleats into her starched apron. She smiled when she saw that Catherine was awake, and got up to lean over her.

'You're feeling better?'

Catherine lifted her wrist and tried to concentrate on her watch. 'What time is it?'

'Three-thirty.'

'Three-thirty!' Catherine was horrified. 'Have I slept for more than three hours?'

'Yes, miz,' Susie nodded.

'I—' Catherine hesitated. 'Where is—everyone?'

Susie frowned. 'There's only you here right now, Miz Fulton. Miz Royal, she phoned to say she was having lunch at the Prentiss house, and Mr Royal, he left over an hour ago.'

'And—and Miss Prentiss?'

'She stay a few minutes after Mr Royal leave, and then she says she's going, too.'

Catherine absorbed this. 'Where—where did—Mr Royal go?' she asked, realising her weakness for doing so.

'I think he went back to the beach house, Miz Fulton. I don't really know. He don't tell anybody. He just leave.'

Catherine struggled up on to her elbows. 'Well, you can go now, Susie. I'll be fine.'

Susie looked doubtful. 'Mr Royal, he say you shouldn't be left alone. Not today, leastways.'

Tears pricked at Catherine's eyes at this fleeting glimpse of Jared's sense of responsibility towards her. But she managed to blink them back, and swung her feet to the floor.

'Honestly, Susie, it—it must just have been a touch of the sun. I—feel quite all right now.'

'You sure?'

Catherine nodded, and the girl moved reluctantly towards the door. But after she had gone, it was simpler to acknowledge weakness, and Catherine bent her head into her hands. Of course, it was too much sun which had upset her—that, and the violence of the emotions Jared had aroused inside her. But she doubted that Jared would ever believe it. And who could blame him? She wondered if he had asked Laura to stay until she woke. Was that why Laura had left after he did? Had the girl chosen this way to show a spark of independence?

With a sigh, Catherine tried to get up from the bed. But to her dismay, her legs buckled under her and she was obliged to crawl back on to the pillows, feeling more alone than she had ever done in her whole life.

In fact, she spent three days in bed.

When Elizabeth returned home and discovered what had happened, she was not to be deterred from calling a doctor. The dark-skinned physician gave Catherine a thorough examination and then pronounced the opinion that she had developed a mild attack of sunstroke. He insisted on at least forty-eight hours' bed rest in a darkened room, and Catherine was certainly too weak to argue with him. But there was no pleasure lying alone with her thoughts, and as her strength gradually returned, she longed to escape from this house which had become a kind of prison to her.

Laura called to see her on her second day in bed. As expected, she made no reference to the events precipitating Catherine's illness, and instead talked incessantly about the plans for the wedding. Catherine wondered if Laura realised what she was doing, and decided that she probably did. She appeared to live life at a very shallow level, and anything likely to disturb the surface calm was deliberately ignored. Listening to her describe her ideas for the bridesmaids' dresses, Catherine was dismayed at the pain she was inflicting, and in her weakness it wasn't easy to hide her feelings. Perhaps Laura knew this, she thought bitterly. There was more than one way of seeking revenge.

Elizabeth was a little more subtle in her approach. Her concern, she said, was that Catherine should be well enough to attend the party the Prentisses were giving in a week's time. It would be a shame, she exclaimed, if Catherine couldn't be there to share in the fun.

Marion Prentiss sent her a bouquet of roses and her wishes for her speedy recovery. Everyone was being very kind, but Catherine doubted their sincerity. All of these women had their own reasons for wishing her well, but they were not the simple ones they alleged.

On the fourth day after her collapse, Catherine was well enough to get up and sit in an armchair on her balcony. The breeze blowing off the Atlantic brought the smell of salt strongly to her nostrils, and she could taste its sharpness against her skin. The morning sun gave the ocean a coral tinge, glinting off the breakers that thundered their way shoreward.

The sound of a car coming up the drive was an intrusion on the quiet air. Earlier only the sounds of the insects among the flowers and the occasional plop of a fly hitting the surface of the pool had disturbed the stillness, but the drone of the engine was increasing rapidly.

Then the engine was cut off and a car door slammed. Catherine's nerves tensed. Who could it be? Laura, most likely, she conceded with a sigh. She hadn't been over the day before, so she could be expected to put in an appearance.

Then there was a tap at her bedroom door. She turned her head. 'Come in!' she called, her eyes widening when Susie came into the room instead of Jared's fiancée.

Susie looked flushed. 'You've a visitor, Miz Fulton,' she exclaimed hurriedly. 'Mr Dexter. He's asked to see you.'

'John Dexter?' Catherine's relief was ludicrous. 'Oh, yes, yes, I'd like to see him.' She looked down doubtfully at her blue silk dressing robe. 'But not like this. Will you ask him to give me five minutes, and I'll come down.'

'Oh, but Miz Fulton, do you think you ought?' Susie was concerned. 'Miz Royal, she said you'd be staying in your room today.'

'I'm all right, Susie,' Catherine exclaimed impatiently, and then gave a sheepish smile, remembering the other occasion she had said the same. 'All right, I know I said that before, but I mean it this time. Look!' She rose to her feet and did a light pirouette. 'There—does that reassure you?'

Susie still looked doubtful. 'Well, would you like me to help you downstairs?'

'I'm not an old lady, Susie! No. Go on, tell Mr Dexter, I won't be long.'

It didn't take long to rinse her face and hands and put

on some panties and a soft jersey tunic. The cream silk skirt swung softly against her legs, and it was good to feel normal again. John was waiting in the parlour, and she was satisfied with her appearance when he showed his evident admiration.

'What's this I hear about you having sunstroke?' he demanded, by way of a greeting, and she relaxed completely.

'Just a mild attack,' she conceded smilingly. 'But what are you doing here? And how did you find out?'

'I had dinner with some friends of the Prentisses last evening. Your name was mentioned. I'd have come sooner if I'd known. You haven't returned any of my telephone calls,' he added reproachfully.

Catherine sighed, sinking down on to a low couch. 'I haven't really had much opportunity.'

'Don't give me that!' John pulled a face at her. 'So—how are you?'

Catherine couldn't resist it. 'How do I look?'

'Marvellous,' returned John steadily. 'Are you going to the party on Friday?'

Catherine shrugged her slim shoulders. 'I don't know. That depends.'

'On what?'

Catherine looked up at him. 'Are you going?'

'Is that an invitation?'

She laughed. 'No. I'm just asking.'

'I'll go—if I can escort you.'

'Oh, John!' She looked at him gratefully. 'You're so good for my ego.'

He came down on the couch beside her then, taking one of her hands in both of his. 'I could be more than that, Catherine. Do you realise, I've thought of you more than any girl I've ever met? Have you thought about me?'

Catherine tried to disentangle her fingers, but he wouldn't

126

let her. She could hardly admit that since the night of the party she had thought of no one but Jared.

'John,' she murmured protestingly. 'Don't—don't try to rush things. Give it time . . .'

'But it's never hit me like this before,' he told her urgently, his eyes searching her face. 'I've known dozens of girls, I'll admit it, but never one like you.'

'Oh, John!' Catherine felt frustrated. She needed him, but as a friend, not a lover!

'Am I intruding?'

Jared strode unsmilingly into the room, and if he was intruding, he obviously had no intention of withdrawing. Catherine was shocked. She had not heard his arrival, and she wondered what he was doing here. Had he finished the commission? Or was this just another visit? In close-fitting suede pants and a matching black shirt, he was more formally dressed at least.

John rose awkwardly to his feet, but Catherine remained where she was on the couch, concentrating her attention on her hands, now clasped together in her lap. She wondered how much of their conversation he had over-heard, and what interpretation he had put on that.

'Hello, Jared!' John greeted him politely. 'I didn't know you were here. I understood you were working down at the beach house.'

'Did you?' Jared's voice was chilling. 'And who told you that?'

'Why, Laura, as a matter of fact. I saw her a few days ago at the clubhouse.'

Jared inclined his head. 'I see.' Then he shifted his attention to Catherine. 'Ought you to be out of bed?'

His scathing tone caught her on the raw, and she looked up at him angrily. 'I'm not an invalid!'

'But you have been ill,' he corrected her coldly, holding

127

her gaze. 'I heard something about—sunstroke?'

'That's right.'

His scepticism was denigrating. 'Really?'

Catherine bent her head. She had sampled his particular brand of cruelty before, but she had never been so vulnerable.

'Catherine's had a pretty rough time, so I hear.' John was quaintly gallant in her defence, an unusual role for him, she guessed. 'Too much sun can be pretty nasty!'

'I'm sure.'

Jared had taken up a stance in front of the screened stone fireplace, and it was obvious from his manner that he had no intention of leaving them alone again.

John, sensing this, looked regretfully down at Catherine. 'Well, I suppose I'd better be going. I don't want to tire you on your first day out of bed.'

'You're not tiring me, John,' she protested, getting to her feet, but Jared chose to differ.

'I think Dexter's right,' he remarked, moving to press the bell by the door. 'You mustn't—overdo it.'

Catherine turned her back on him. 'It was nice of you to call, John—and about that party you mentioned ...'

'Yes?' John looked at her eagerly.

'... I'll come,' she said quickly, ignoring Jared's harsh intake of breath behind her. 'Ring me on Thursday. We can make the final arrangements then.'

'I surely will.' John's expression as he said goodbye to Jared had a trace of smugness about it now, but Catherine couldn't help that. 'Look after yourself.'

Susie appeared in the doorway. 'You rang, Mr Royal?' she asked, her eyes wide and filled with speculation.

'Yes, I did, Susie.' Jared nodded slowly. 'Show Mr Dexter out, would you?'

Catherine exchanged another smile with her visitor, and

then Susie escorted him out of the room. After the sound of their footsteps had died away, Jared walked grimly towards the double doors, and taking one handle in each hand, he firmly closed them. Then he turned to face her.

'What is this fiasco about your having sunstroke?' he demanded fiercely.

'Fiasco?' Catherine shook her head, remarkably calm in the circumstances. 'I don't know what you mean.'

'Yes, you do.' He moved away from the doors. 'We both know it was not sunstroke that caused that moment of unconsciousness!'

'Do we?' Catherine refused to prolong this charade. 'You mean your brutality caused my collapse?'

'No, I do not mean that!' he snapped angrily, coming to stand barely a foot away from her, intimidating both in nearness and size. 'You know exactly what I mean. I don't have to draw pictures. You fainted because of your condition, and you know it. Oh, I'm not denying that my behaviour may have had something to do with it, but *sunstroke*!' He raked a savage hand through his hair. 'My God, however did you get away with it?'

Catherine resisted the temptation to back away from him. 'My condition, as you put it, is a fallacy!' she stated clearly.

Jared's brow creased. 'What's that supposed to mean?'

'It means I was lying. I'm not pregnant. I never was.'

'What?' He stared at her incredulously. 'God, you have a nerve, you really do!'

'Why? For deceiving you? I couldn't resist——'

'*No!*' He swore obscenely. 'Not for deceiving me! You don't really expect me to believe you, do you?'

'Why not? You did before.'

'You were not lying before.'

'I'm not lying now,' she corrected him, quivering as his

129

anger intensified.

'You really expect me to accept that you made the whole thing up?'

'No. You did.'

'What?'

He took a threatening step towards her and now she did back away. 'It's true,' she cried. 'You started it. You accused me of—of behaving in a way that invited trouble.'

'You don't learn, do you?' he asked violently. 'Your father wrote to me, remember? Are you denying that he was concerned about you?'

She took a deep breath. 'No, I'm not denying that. But did you ever trouble to find out why?'

'I didn't need to, did I?'

Catherine's fists clenched convulsively. 'Isn't that just typical of you? It never occurred to you that there might be some other reason than the obvious one, did it?'

'Frankly, no.'

'Frankly, no!' she mimicked him, putting the width of the couch between them. 'Oh, you make me sick! You think you know women so well! Well, let me tell you, you don't know me at all!'

Jared's expression was scornful. 'Not yet, perhaps,' he conceded grimly.

'You never will!'

'Won't I?' He gripped the back of the couch, and for a heart-stopping moment, she thought he intended throwing it aside to reach her. 'You can't deny that if Laura hadn't come upon us as she did, you'd have let me finish what I'd started!'

'I do deny it!' she gasped hotly, and his lips curled.

'Self-deception, Catherine,' he sneered. 'You practise it a lot.'

'So do you!' she retorted, goaded beyond reason. 'Pretending there's nothing between you and your stepmother!'

Now she had gone too far. She saw that immediately. But this time he had the advantage. The windows were closed, and in her weakened condition, he reached the doors long before she did.

'Oh, no,' he ground out angrily, his fingers closing painfully round her upper arm. 'Not this time. I'm tempted—God, how I'm tempted—to put you over my knee and administer the thrashing you so richly deserve for that, but unfortunately I find there are limits to my behaviour. Nevertheless, you will take that back, or I will find some method of punishment equally unpleasant!'

Catherine was trembling. It had all been too much for her, and with an exclamation he put his free hand against her forehead. She was burning up, and the coolness of his fingers was so heavenly that when he would have taken them away again, she put up her hand and held them there.

'You really are ill, aren't you?' he demanded savagely. 'Dear God, Catherine, why didn't you tell them the truth? Were you ashamed to do so? Do you want me to do it for you?'

'No!' She tore herself away from him. 'Ju—just leave me alone!' She swayed unsteadily. It was useless trying to reason with him. He simply refused to listen to her. 'I'm not ill. Just—frustrated!'

'Perhaps you ought to go back to bed,' he suggested quietly, and his concern was almost worse than his anger had been. 'Would you like me to help you?'

'And if I say yes, will that be misconstrued, too?' she asked bitterly. 'No, I'm not going to bed. And I don't need your assistance.'

He took a step towards her and she stiffened, but then he turned abruptly aside, saying unexpectedly: 'This man—Tony Bainbridge; do you love him?'

She was surprised he remembered Tony's name, but then he had a remarkable sense of recall.

She hesitated a moment, and then, supporting herself with the doorknob, she answered flatly: 'No.'

He half turned to look at her. 'No?' he demanded harshly.

'That's right.'

'Then in God's name, why—why did you——'

'Do you love Laura?' she asked daringly, and he ran a weary hand round the back of his neck.

'I don't have to,' he said heavily, and she was still staring at him when the door was propelled open behind her, almost knocking her off her feet. It was Elizabeth who stood in the aperture, flushed and vaguely dishevelled for once, in her working clothes, with obviously little satisfaction in finding them alone together.

'You're back, Jared,' she stated unnecessarily. 'I was—surprised when Susie told me.'

'Were you?' Catherine heard a note of impatience in Jared's voice. 'I don't see why. Considering all the plans you've been making for me in my absence.'

Elizabeth glanced angrily at Catherine. 'What has she been saying?'

'Catherine?' Now he looked surprised. 'Catherine hasn't said anything. Why? What could she have said?'

Elizabeth made a frustrated gesture. 'I just thought—oh, it's not important.'

'What's this party Laura's told me about?'

Elizabeth cast another meaningful glance in Catherine's direction. 'Can't we discuss this later, darling?'

'I can go,' said Catherine at once, but Jared's look checked her.

'It's not a private affair, is it, Liz?' he inquired, coolly. 'As I understand it, half the island has been invited.'

Elizabeth expelled her breath noisily. 'Oh, all right. It's

just a party Marion wants to give for the two of you.'

'With your assistance?'

'I admit—I thought it was a good idea.'

'Well, I don't,' said Jared cuttingly. 'Cancel it!'

'Cancel it?' Elizabeth was staggered, and there was venom in the look she exchanged with Catherine. She would not easily forgive the girl for witnessing her humiliation. 'I can't cancel it. The invitations have already gone out.'

'Then you'll have to get them back again, won't you?' Jared told her unfeelingly. 'You should have consulted me before going ahead with those kind of arrangements.'

'But, darling, we discussed it . . .'

'Correction—we discussed the wedding. And that's something else I want to talk about.'

'Oh, not now, Jared.'

Elizabeth was imploring, and he seemed to take pity on her as he nodded, hunching his shoulders and pushing his hands deep into the pockets of his pants.

'All right.' He paused. 'And now I'm taking Catherine out for lunch.' His tone brooked no argument, his eyes challenging Catherine's to deny him, but she could only stand by weakly while he dealt with his stepmother.

'You're—taking—Catherine—*out*—for lunch?' Elizabeth echoed faintly.

'Yes.' He inclined his head. 'You have no objections, I trust?'

Elizabeth probably had dozens, thought Catherine, unable to keep pace with his swift changes of mood. Why was he taking her out for lunch? What did it all mean? Did he believe her after all?

'Laura may be coming over,' Elizabeth pointed out uneasily.

'I'm sure you'll tell her where I've gone,' returned her

stepson briefly. 'Catherine? Are you ready?'

Catherine wasn't at all sure she ought to go with him. She was almost convinced she was still running a temperature, and his company did nothing to relieve that. And yet how could she refuse him, when she so badly wanted to go with him?

Elizabeth made one last attempt to stay them. 'Catherine has been in bed for the last three days, Jared. I don't think Doctor Matthews would approve of her getting up and going straight out, however well she feels.' She surveyed the girl coldly. 'And quite honestly, I don't think she looks at all well.'

Catherine squared her shoulders. 'I'll be fine, thank you, Mrs Royal.' She looked at Jared. 'I'm ready. Shall we go?'

The convertible stood on the drive, dusty with sand thrown up on it from the beach. Before starting the engine, Jared raised the hood to protect her from the glare of the sun, and she gave him a surprised look of gratitude.

'I agree with Liz, actually,' he muttered roughly, levering his length behind the wheel. 'You ought not to have come out.'

Catherine gasped. 'But—you asked me!'

'I know I did.'

'You—wanted me to refuse?'

He gave her an impatient look. 'Is that likely?' He flicked the ignition. 'What I want and what I achieve— don't always sympathise.'

Catherine was confused. 'You wanted me to come?'

Jared glanced sideways at her. 'Do I have to answer that?' he demanded, and the naked passion in his eyes constricted her throat. She shook her head, and with an evident effort, he resumed his concentration on his driving.

He turned south on the coast road, and Catherine was content just to sit beside him and relax. He shifted slightly so that his thigh was touching hers, and every time he moved his leg, she was made intensely aware of him. Realising she had to cool the situation before they arrived wherever he was taking her, she ventured softly:

'Did you—did you finish the commission?'

Jared's fingers tightened on the wheel. 'No.'

'Oh.' Catherine licked her lips. 'I'm sorry.'

'So am I.' Jared heaved a deep breath. 'How are you feeling now?'

Catherine looked back over her shoulder at a group of dark-skinned children cycling along the road. 'Aren't they adorable?' she exclaimed, forcing what she hoped was a casual tone. Then: 'I'm fine, honestly.'

'You like children?' he inquired harshly.

Catherine flushed. 'Of course. Don't you?'

'I guess I'm going to have to,' he retorted enigmatically, and swung the car across the road and through the gates of an hotel set in semi-tropical surroundings, and boasting a magnificent view of the ocean.

Jared was recognised, and while a table was being prepared for them in the restaurant, they went for a drink. One wall of the bar had been rolled aside to give access to the lido area beside the pool, and guests walked about in shorts or bikinis, mingling with more formally clad patrons. Jared suggested they seated themselves at the long red counter, on tall stools, luxuriously shaped like small armchairs.

He ordered long chilled drinks, served in glasses edged with slices of fruit and frosted with ice, and containing a definite tang of alcoholic sharpness. But it was good, and Catherine drank hers thirstily.

'Steady on,' advised Jared dryly, putting a hand on her arm and propelling the glass back on to the bar. 'It's not lemonade.'

135

Catherine smiled. 'I never thought it was.'

Jared's fingers lingered against her skin, his thumb massaging the veins on the inner side of her wrist. 'Would you really have stopped me from making love to you?' he asked softly, his eyes heavy with meaning.

Catherine drew her arm out of his grasp, and gestured futilely towards the pool. 'I can't wait to swim again,' she babbled. 'It seems weeks, not days, since I was in the water. I expect you've swum every day at the beach house, haven't you? And surfed, too. I'd love to be an expert at that——'

'I could teach you,' he said steadily, and chancing a brief look at him, she was devastated by the warmth of his gaze.

'Don't look at me like that, Jared,' she breathed huskily, and he shrugged and turned his stool so that its back was against the bar, surveying the scene around the pool with a slightly jaded contemplation.

A girl in a bikini, who had been stretched out beside a young man on an air bed, got to her feet just then and seeing Jared, waved vigorously. Then, nudging the man at her feet with her toe, she stepped over his bulk and came into the bar towards them.

'Jared!' she exclaimed, bending over him to kiss his cheek and giving him the full benefit of her cleavage. 'Jared Royal! I've only been back in Bridgetown since Saturday and what do I hear? Jared Royal is getting married at last! I couldn't believe it.' Her gaze shifted to Catherine, and then she looked frankly embarrassed. 'Oh, I mean—I thought—where's Laura, Jared?'

'At home, I expect,' returned Jared lazily, getting to his feet. 'Catherine, this is Angela Motson. Angela, I'd like you to meet my—my *ward*.'

He used the word deliberately, and watching him Catherine encountered the mocking challenge of his stare. Angela, meanwhile, was obviously astonished, and she looked round impatiently for her escort to join them. The young man was slowly getting to his feet, and Catherine recognised Andy David, one of Laura's friends, who had attended the party at Amaryllis.

He and Jared greeted one another, and he smiled at Catherine. 'Feeling better?' he asked. 'Laura told me you'd been smitten by the heat.'

'I'm much better, thank you,' Catherine replied politely, and Angela, having recovered her composure, exclaimed: 'Are you two eating in the hotel?'

'As a matter of fact we are,' Jared agreed, and Catherine's heart sank when Angela suggested they should all have lunch together.

'I've just spent three months in the States,' she explained, for Catherine's benefit, 'and I can't wait to catch up on all the news. How about it, Jared?'

Jared glanced at Catherine, but she was looking down at her hands, and he gave a casual shrug. 'All right,' he said, as she had known he would. 'So long as we can get away by two. I have to be at Seawell by two-thirty.'

'The airport?'

Angela raised her eyebrows, but as Jared said nothing more, she was forced to let it go. Catherine was curious, too, but she guessed Jared was going to the airport to collect some painting equipment. Maybe that was why he had taken this day off from finishing the commission. It was a logical assumption, and it succeeded in destroying her already depleted store of confidence.

The meal was delicious. Prawns with melon, steaks and salad, and a trifle flavoured with brandy. But Catherine ate next to nothing. She felt choked with emotion, aware, as he obviously was not, of their brief time together slipping away.

Only once during that long meal did she look up to find

Jared staring at her, but when she tried to communicate her feelings to him, he looked away again, and a moment later was laughing heartily at something Angela had said.

However, when the waiter came to ask them if they had enjoyed the food and to inquire whether they would like coffee, Jared pushed back his chair.

'I think we'll have to skip coffee, if you don't mind, Catherine,' he said abruptly, and Catherine didn't mind at all. She got obediently to her feet, gesturing Andy to re-remain seated when he would have risen, and walked round the table to join Jared.

'Oh, must you go?' Angela was evidently disappointed. 'It's only ten minutes to the hour.'

'I'm sorry.' Jared was adamant. His hand curved round Catherine's upper arm. 'We'll see you some other time.'

'At the party!' exclaimed Angela enthusiastically. 'My invitation was waiting when I got back. I'm looking forward to it.'

Catherine and Jared exchanged glances, and then he gave a slight shake of his head as if to indicate a negative re-action. 'So long!' he said non-committally, and propelling Catherine before him, walked out of the restaurant.

But once in the car, his actions bespoke his annoyance. 'I expect you think I should have told Angela there's not going to be any party, don't you?' he demanded.

Catherine shifted her shoulders against the soft warm upholstery. 'I can't answer that,' she protested.

'No? Well, I didn't feel like entering into those kind of explanations with her!'

'You don't have to justify yourself to me.'

'Don't I?' He didn't start the engine, but half turned in his seat towards her, one arm along the back of hers. 'Don't I? So why were you giving me the cold shoulder all through lunch?'

'I wasn't doing that,' she cried. 'Besides, you seemed contented enough talking to your old girl-friend.'

'Angela is not an "old girl-friend".'

'Well, a young girl-friend, then,' retorted Catherine tautly.

'Not that either. She's a friend of Laura's. Would you have had me be rude to her?'

'It's nothing to do with me.'

'Damn you, it's everything to do with you,' he swore violently, and turning, he started the car savagely, releasing the brake, and churning up the drive with spinning tyres.

Catherine clutched the edge of her seat as they approached the gates, convinced Jared would never negotiate them at this speed. But long before there was any danger, he had slowed, and they turned out on to the coast road again with controlled expertise.

'Jared, why did you ask me out to lunch?' she asked, helplessly staring at him. 'I only seem to make you angry.'

Jared drew a harsh breath. 'Because,' he said, his tone containing traces of self-derision, 'because, fool that I am, I've let you get under my skin. To the extent that I can't seem to think of anything but you!'

'Jared . . .'

'I can't work, I can't sleep! That's rich, isn't it?' he demanded, his lips twisting. 'I guess you could say that was why I resented what you did to me all those years ago. Maybe even then I knew I was fighting a losing battle.'

'Oh, Jared!' She was incredulous. 'Jared, I don't know what to say.' But her pulses were racing, and it was not just the aftermath of her illness that was making the blood thunder in her head.

'You could say—you're not entirely indifferent to me,' he muttered harshly, and her heart almost stopped beating when his hand slid possessively down her thigh to her knee. She put both her hands over his, and with an uncharacter-

139

istic disregard for other drivers, he stood on his brakes and, turning, pulled her into his arms.

She barely had time to say his name before his mouth covered hers, and the probing intimacy of his touch drove all coherent thought from her head.

'Oh, God!' he muttered at last, lifting his head to the sound of car horns and hooters, the well-meaning laughter of some road-users, and the not-so-well-meaning impatience of others. 'I want you all to myself, and instead we're stuck in this public place, providing free entertainment for the masses!'

Catherine smoothed her hair back behind her ears. 'Let's go down to the beach,' she breathed huskily, but with a grim shake of his head, he released the clutch and drove on.

'There's something I have to do first,' he said flatly.

'What?' Catherine bent her head. 'Is—is it Laura? Are we meeting her at the airport?'

He glanced at her strangely. 'I wish to God it were,' he ground out savagely, and she moved her shoulders in bewilderment.

'What is it? Jared, you're not still thinking——'

'I'm trying not to think,' he told her through clenched teeth. 'I never thought I could do it, but I realise I'll have to.'

'Have to what?' She knelt on the seat beside him. 'Jared —darling, what is it?'

His eyes darkened at the involuntary endearment, but then they were entering the airport complex and he had to give all his attention to his driving. Catherine swung her legs to the floor again, staring out at the incoming Boeing that was making its final run. No matter what Jared had said, there was an awful feeling of apprehension invading her system, and his determination to get to the airport had assumed the proportions of an obsession. What did he want here? What was it he had to do? And why should she feel so sure it had something to do with her?

He parked the convertible, and Catherine looked at him doubtfully. 'Do you want me to stay here?'

'No.' Jared got out of the car, and walked round to open her door. 'Come with me.'

'But where are we going?' she exclaimed, as they crossed to the airport buildings. 'Jared, what are we doing here?'

'You'll see.' Jared had become curiously remote, and there was a tautness about his features which had not been there earlier. 'Come on, it looks like the flight's landed.'

Catherine was asking: 'What flight?' as they entered the reception hall, but Jared strode ahead, looking about him, obviously searching for whoever it was they had come to meet. Catherine followed him slowly. She didn't understand what was going on, and the anxiety inside her was strengthening all the time. Although that was something else she didn't understand either.

'*Cat!* Cat, old love! Here I am! Turning up again like the veritable bad penny!'

Catherine swung round. Surely she hadn't mistaken that voice? 'Tony!' she gasped, and hearing her involuntary exclamation, Jared turned, too. 'Tony, for heaven's sake,' she cried. 'What are you doing here?'

Jared was walking back towards them, and Catherine could see how pale he was beneath his tan. 'You are Tony Bainbridge?' he said, in a strange uneven voice. Then he looked at Catherine. 'This is—Tony?'

'Didn't he tell you I was coming, old love?' Tony looked at her, too, and Catherine, dry-mouthed, shook her head.

'I wanted to——' Jared broke off, his face so grim it was frightening. 'I didn't realise that—that you——'

'That I was a cripple?' asked Tony cheerfully, from the austerity of his wheelchair. 'Didn't Cat tell you? No, I can

141

see she didn't. Well, I'm afraid I am. Useless from the waist down, I'm sorry to say.' He winked in his usual good-humoured fashion. 'That's why Manners always goes everywhere with me, don't you, Manners?'

A tall thin man appeared from behind a rack of magazines and approached them. He was a middle-aged man, balding and bespectacled, but with his employer's sense of humour.

He smiled at Catherine and nodded at Jared. 'Good afternoon,' he remarked. 'Nice to see you again, Miss Fulton. Wasn't it kind of—of Mr Royal to invite us out here?'

CHAPTER NINE

'I appear to have put my foot in it, don't I, old love? Metaphorically speaking, of course.'

Tony spoke from the bed, but his words didn't stop Catherine's pacing.

'Why did you come out here, Tony?' she exclaimed helplessly, spreading her hands. 'You know you don't like leaving London!'

'That's some line in welcomes,' observed Tony dryly. 'I received an invitation. From your lord and master.'

'He's not my lord and master!'

'Isn't he? He acts like he is.'

'Yes—well, what he acts like and what he is, are two entirely different things.'

'You know him that well, huh?'

'I don't know him well at all.'

Tony shrugged. 'How was I to know you weren't behind his invitation? Why the hell didn't he tell you?'

Catherine sighed, and came to stand at the end of the bed, holding the post with both hands. 'What did he tell you, Tony? What was his reason for asking you out here?'

Tony grimaced. 'I forget his exact words. Something about you being—ill? Have you been ill?'

'A little. Just a touch of the sun, that's all.'

'You'll have to watch that.'

'Oh, Tony, what else did he say?'

'It was only a telegram, old love. You can't say a lot in a telegram.'

'So that was all? That I'd been ill?'

Tony frowned. 'Well, he made it sound as if you needed me, know what I mean? Though why he should have thought that, I can't imagine.'

'I can.'

Catherine spoke under her breath, hunching her shoulders, and turning away. She could imagine only too well. Jared was convinced she was expecting a child—Tony's child, he presumed. He had brought Tony out here to face his responsibilities. That was the way things were done here. But now he must know that Tony could not possibly father any child.

But why had he arranged this secretly? Why hadn't he told her what he was planning? Given her a chance to persuade him he was wasting his time? Why had he behaved today as if he loved her, and then produced the one man she might conceivably be expected to care about? It didn't make sense. Unless . . .

She paced restlessly across to the open french doors. They had given Tony rooms on the ground floor of the house, enabling him to come and go in his wheelchair without difficulty. Manners was next door, unpacking their belongings, but he had insisted that Tony should rest for a while before dinner. He didn't approve of Catherine being here, but she felt that if she didn't talk to somebody she would go mad.

Coming back from the airport, she had travelled in the back of the car with Manners, it being easier for Tony to manoeuvre himself into the front seat. His wheelchair was collapsible, and had fitted without too much difficulty into the spacious boot. But even sitting behind Jared, she had been conscious of his anger. It had been there in the polite, but clipped, conversation, he had held with Tony—in the controlled suppression of his driving—in the stiffened tautness of his shoulders, the grimly-held set of his head.

144

She had wanted to slide her hands over his shoulders, she had wanted to press her face into the dark hair which overlapped his collar at the back, to feel his instant response to the pressure of her body.

But instead she had to remain in her seat, silent, answering only when Tony deliberately brought her into the conversation.

When they arrived back at the house, Jared had issued brusque instructions for rooms to be made ready for their guests, and Lily and the other servants had scurried around doing his bidding. It would have been no problem accommodating two people on the first floor, but preparing ground floor rooms had necessitated the removal of certain pieces of furniture, and the installation of others. Tony had been apologetic, endearingly so, Catherine had felt, with a renewal of her affection for him, but Elizabeth, once the initial introductions were over, had proved to be most welcoming. It was no trouble, she had insisted, accommodating any friend of Catherine's, but remembering the other woman's behaviour before she and Jared left that morning, Catherine knew she read the obvious explanation for this situation into Jared's actions. And that brought her back to her own question—why had Jared done it?

Unless ... And this was the painful part, unless, in spite of his professed attraction for her, he intended going ahead with his plans and marrying Laura. Perhaps he had seen this as a sure way of getting her, Catherine, off his back. Maybe he resented the power she appeared to have over him. Certainly it had seemed that way in the past. But today ...

Better forget today, she thought dully. Better forget everything but the fact that Jared was engaged to Laura, and she was committed to helping Tony raise enough money to build his rehabilitation centre.

'What is it, old love?'

Tony shifted restlessly on the bed, and turning to face him, Catherine felt a pang of guilt at his innocent involvement in all this.

'Nothing,' she said, forcing a smile and determinedly approaching the bed. 'I'll go and leave you. You get some rest. We can talk later.'

Tony stretched out a hand and imprisoned one of hers. 'You're in love with the guy, aren't you?' he stated quietly. 'Don't try to deny it. I know you too well.'

Catherine sighed. 'Tony, Jared is engaged to be married to a girl called Laura Prentiss. You'll probably meet her this evening. I heard Elizabeth say she was going to invite her for dinner.'

Tony gave her an old-fashioned look. 'Since when has an engagement ring prevented one person from being attracted to another? Or a wedding ring, either, for that matter?'

'Tony, please . . .'

'I think you know why he brought me out here.'

'I don't.' She could feel the warm colour invading her cheeks. 'Well, at least—perhaps part of the reason.'

'Which is?'

'I can't tell you, Tony.'

'Why not?'

She bent her head. 'It was—stupid!'

'What was stupid?'

'Something I did. Tony, please, don't ask me.'

'But I am asking you.' He looked up at her steadily. 'Don't you think that perhaps you owe me that?'

She heaved a sigh. 'You won't like it.'

'I'm prepared for the worst.'

'I——' She pressed her lips tightly together for a moment. 'I—I let Jared think I—I was pregnant!'

'*What?*' Tony dropped her hand to stare at her disbelievingly. 'You did what? In God's name, what are you

146

talking about?'

'You see?' She shook her head. 'I told you you wouldn't like it.'

'I certainly don't, but I want to know why you did it.'

'Tony, Manners said you had to rest——'

'Do you think I could rest with this on my mind?' Tony gave her an exasperated stare. 'Come on, sit down.' He patted the bed beside him. 'You might as well unburden yourself.'

'Oh, Tony!' Catherine sank down on to the bed and burst into tears, burying her face in her hands and sobbing as if her heart would break.

Tony levered himself across the bed to her side, putting his arms around her and drawing her comfortably against his broad chest. 'It's all right, old love,' he murmured huskily, stroking her hair. 'It's all right. Just take it easy. From the beginning ...'

With stumbling incoherence, Catherine eventually poured out the whole story—her schoolgirl crush on the older man who had been a friend of her father's, Jared's attitude on her arrival in Barbados and her reckless submission, her subsequent relationship with him ...

Tony was silent when she had finished, and she lifted her head to look at him anxiously. 'You're angry with me?'

Tony shook his head. 'Impatient, perhaps,' he conceded. 'Oh, Catherine! You always were an impulsive little fool! Why didn't you explain why your father had written to Royal? Why did you let him think you lived the life of Riley? God Almighty, Jack Fulton has something to answer for!'

'Don't speak of Daddy like that,' she protested.

'Well, it's true. Money was his god, but it was never yours. You should have explained what he was afraid you would do.'

147

'I couldn't.' Catherine drew away from him, dabbing her eyes with a corner of the coverlet. 'Anyway, it's all been my fault——'

'Well, I think Royal's behaved like a bastard!'

'Tony!'

'I do. Just imagine if everything had been as he expected—if I had been the kind of man he imagined me to be. You here pregnant, and me in London having a good time. What a nerve bringing me out here to see you! I mean —well, we mightn't have wanted to see one another. He's out of touch. He doesn't realise there are thousands of women nowadays bringing up children without what they consider to be the encumbrance of a husband. You might have been one of those!'

'Well, I'm not,' Catherine stated flatly, getting up from the bed. 'And besides, I don't think you appreciate what kind of man Jared is. It's against his principles, I think, to allow a child to be born out of wedlock if he might have been able to do something about it.'

'Oh, honestly?' Tony looked sceptical. 'What kind of principles allow him to make love to a woman he thought was pregnant, while his own fiancée is forced to look on? I feel sorry for her—not him. And bringing me out here! It's feudal! Like I said before, I think he's a bastard!'

And on this unhappy note, Catherine left him. She had to admit—the facts were damning. But the facts were one-dimensional, life was not.

She wondered if Jared might try to speak to her before dinner, but he did not come near. She rested on her bed for a while, and then bathed and changed, taking some time over deciding what to wear. She chose a simple black gown, made of draped jersey, with a halter neckline, that left most of her shoulders and her arms bare.

As she sat at the vanity unit, stroking mascara on to long

dark lashes, she reflected on her own sense of weariness. This had been a strenuous day for someone recovering from an illness, however slight, and had Tony not been expecting to see her, she would have made some excuse and remained in her room. Her bed was very inviting, but somehow she had to find the strength to face Jared, and perhaps the sooner that was over, the better she would feel. But what would happen now, she didn't dare to speculate.

Laura and her parents were just arriving as Catherine came down the stairs, and the girl made a beeline for her.

'What's going on?' she exclaimed. 'Elizabeth has told us that a friend of yours has arrived from London. Is that right? Who is he? Did you know he was coming?'

'I—why, not exactly . . .'

Catherine was struggling to find words when Jared came strolling into the hall from the direction of the library. He greeted the Prentisses politely, shaking hands with Laura's father, and then allowed his cold gaze to take in the two girls. Laura left Catherine to go to her fiancé, sliding her arm possessively through his and saying:

'Darling, I was just asking Catherine about her visitor. Perhaps you can enlighten us, as she seems too bemused by his arrival to explain.'

Jared's features were taut and controlled. 'I arranged it,' he said expressionlessly. 'I thought—Catherine—was missing her friends.'

Catherine's eyes darted indignantly to his face, but his expression deterred any contradiction. She stared at him helplessly, trying to see behind that cold mask he had adopted, but it was useless. He was as remote as he had ever been.

'Well, wasn't that thoughtful?'

Marion Prentiss was speaking now, removing her fur stole and handing it to Susie who had come to stand behind

149

them, smiling comfortably at her daughter and Jared. In apricot satin, she looked plumper than ever, and Laura, in her lemon taffeta, looked like a pale reflection of her mother.

Elizabeth appeared behind her stepson. 'Marion!' she exclaimed warmly. 'Gerald! And Laura! Come in, come in. Come and meet our guest of honour, Catherine's— friend, Tony Bainbridge.'

They all moved towards the library, Catherine and Mr Prentiss bringing up the rear. The next few minutes were taken up with introductions, and Tony, goodnatured and confident, soon had them all responding to his personality. All, that is, except Jared. He remained aloof, mixing drinks and handing them around, taking his own and standing on the hearth to drink it silently, viewing the scene around him over the rim of his glass. Although Tony made sure she was involved in the conversation, Catherine was supremely conscious of Jared's detachment, and in spite of his coldness, she ached to go to him.

Laura, for once, seemed less obsessed with her fiancé. It was obvious she had never met anyone like Tony before, and remembering her own immediate attraction to him, Catherine could understand this. No one could help but admire the way he could dismiss his own disabilities with an airy shake of his head, assuring everyone around him that he considered himself fortunate to be alive. When he was eleven years old, he had been aboard a plane which had crashed in the mountains of South America, killing his brothers and leaving him paralysed from the waist down. They had been flying out to Peru to join their parents who were on an archaeological dig there. There had been only seven survivors, and although he could make light of it now, Catherine knew there had been times when he had suffered terrible depressions. She had wanted to ensure that he would never feel that way again. That was why she had

150

tried to persuade her father to help finance Tony's plans for a comprehensive rehabilitation centre for the physically handicapped. But Jack Fulton had had little time for charities.

Dinner was served a little later than usual, and not surprisingly, Catherine found herself seated between Tony and Mr Prentiss. Jared and Elizabeth occupied opposite ends of the long dining table, Jared with Laura on his right, and Manners, who had been pressed to join them to make up the numbers, seated between Laura and her mother. It meant that Catherine had to look sideways to see Jared, and as Elizabeth kept coupling her with Tony, the occasions were few.

Surprisingly, when dinner was over and they all adjourned to the pool area for coffee and liqueurs, Laura upset Elizabeth's plans by taking charge of Tony's wheelchair, insisting on propelling it even though he was perfectly capable of doing so himself. Gerald Prentiss had attached himself to Elizabeth, much to her annoyance, Catherine guessed, and as Mrs Prentiss was asking Manners questions about rehabilitation after a serious accident, Catherine found herself conspicuously left with Jared.

He was silent for so long, she thought he did not intend to speak at all, but eventually he said: 'Your friend seems to have made a considerable success!' in a cold hard voice.

Catherine looked unhappily up at him. In a dark blue velvet dinner suit, he had never looked more attractive, and although she felt his own behaviour lacked consistency, she could not let him go on in this way without making some attempt to reach him.

'Jared,' she breathed in a low voice, bending her head so that anyone watching them should not be able to read her lips, 'Why are you behaving like this?'

'Like what?' he inquired flatly.

151

She sighed. 'Don't be obtuse. You know what I mean. I just don't understand, that's all.'

'That's unfortunate.'

'Oh, Jared!' She looked up at him again, frustration darkening her eyes. 'I wish you'd told me.'

'Why?' His eyes glinted coldly. 'Would that have stopped me from making a fool of myself?'

'You haven't made a fool of yourself!'

'Oh, yes, I have.' His expression was contemptuous. 'With your assistance, of course.'

'Jared, I told you I wasn't pregnant. But you wouldn't believe me!'

'It was a little late, wasn't it?'

'It needn't have been. I told you that night on the beach, but you wouldn't listen to me!'

'How foolish of me.'

'Jared, stop it! This afternoon——'

'I don't want to talk about this afternoon.'

'Why not?'

His eyes bored into hers. 'Oh, come on, Catherine. You're not that naïve. You've played me for a fool all the way along the line! How do I know you weren't pregnant when you came out here? There are other men in London, aren't there? Men with all their—faculties? If you think I'd believe anything you said after this——'

'You—you devil——'

'Strong words!' Jared glanced about them, assuring himself that no one had overheard her. 'Keep your voice down. I'd prefer it if it wasn't broadcast across the island that one of my guests is no lady!'

Catherine caught her breath. 'You—you—I don't believe you have any normal feelings! You're just put out—because your goddam pride has been hurt, that's all. You didn't care when you were humiliating Laura, but when it affects you,

152

you don't like it!'

'That's right,' he conceded grimly. 'You've got it in one.'

'What a selfish swine you are!'

'I've had a good teacher.'

'Who? Me? How can you say that? I didn't start this, you did! Insinuating that I—I slept around. That that was what Daddy was concerned about!'

'Wasn't it?'

'No!' His contempt caught her on the raw. 'If you must know, it *was* Tony that Daddy was worried about. But not in the way you thought. Tony wants to open a rehabilitation centre for the physically handicapped. He's got some splendid ideas. I've been trying to persuade Daddy for ages——' She broke off as a wave of nostalgia swept over her. Then she went on: 'Anyway, he knew—he knew he wasn't well. That there was a possibility of him ...' She drew an unsteady breath. 'He was afraid that if anything happened to him, I might give my inheritance away. Or most of it, at least. Money has never meant all that much to me. I can work, if I have to.'

Jared uttered a grim expletive. 'How touching!' It was obvious he didn't believe a word of it.

'It's the truth!' she cried desperately. 'Jared, I wouldn't lie about a thing like that.'

'Wouldn't you?'

For a long gripping moment, his gaze held hers, and then, with an impatient gesture, Jared walked away.

Catherine remained where he had left her. Her knees were knocking, and the weakness she had felt earlier had returned in full measure. It was useless trying to reason with Jared. He simply chose what he saw to be the truth, and stuck to it, ruthlessly. He was cruel and selfish and completely amoral where his own needs were concerned, and she wished to God she never had to see him again ...

CHAPTER TEN

'WE'LL have to be thinking of getting back to London, Manners and me,' said Tony quietly, levering himself up on his elbows and surveying the colourful patio area with reluctant admiration.

'Oh, no!' Catherine rolled on to her stomach on the li-lo beside him, staring at him in dismay. 'Tony, you can't!'

'I'm afraid I'll have to, old love. Do you realise we've been here over a week already? There are things I have to do, activities to be organised. You wouldn't want me to let my committee down, now would you?'

Catherine heaved a sigh. 'I can't bear the idea of what it's going to be like around here after you've gone.'

Tony grimaced. 'I've never been so popular,' he commented dryly.

Catherine looked half ashamed, getting to her knees and pressing her palms down upon them. 'I mean it, Tony. I don't know if I can stand it if you go.'

Tony reached out a hand and pressed her arm. 'Come back with me, then.'

Catherine's eyes flickered. 'Do you mean that?'

'Of course I do. You don't *have* to stay. You're not a ward of court or anything, are you? And by the time Royal could arrange something like that, you could be long gone.'

Catherine turned to sit with her knees drawn up, her arms wrapped around them. 'It's a temptation.'

'Hasn't he spoken to you?'

'Since the night you arrived? No.' She shook her head, only just managing to keep the tremor out of her voice.

Tony swore softly, an unusual thing for him, and she turned her head to smile gratefully at him. A week in the sun had done little to tan Tony's naturally fair complexion, but he had spent several hours with her here, beside the pool, sunbathing. She would miss his undemanding companionship, and the barrier he presented between her and Elizabeth's maliciousness.

Although the older woman must know that whatever had transpired between Catherine and her stepson—they were no longer speaking to one another—she obviously still regarded the girl as a potential rival. Or perhaps enemy was a better word, thought Catherine bitterly. Whatever Jared's feelings, or lack of them, towards his stepmother, Elizabeth still regarded him as her personal property, only willing to lend him out to someone like Laura who would never make demands upon him.

Of Jared himself she had seen little. When he was not in his studio, he was down at the beach house, joining the rest of them only rarely even for meals. He and Tony did not like one another, and although he was polite, his courteousness was tinged with constraint.

Laura remained a frequent visitor, and now Catherine was almost glad to see her. She sometimes seemed the only sane one amongst them, and her admiration for Tony had not decreased. They spent hours discussing the various aspects of disability in all its forms, and Laura had suggestions to make which surprised Catherine in their originality.

'You must come to London and visit the centre when it's completed,' Tony had exclaimed one afternoon, and although Laura had looked doubtful, Catherine had guessed she would really like to have accepted the invitation. But by then she and Jared would be married ...

'Well, I think you'd better come back with me,' Tony was saying now. 'Royal's met me. He knows the worst. He must

155

realise he has nothing to be alarmed about.'

Catherine made a stifled sound. 'He doesn't believe that either.'

'What?' Tony was surprised. 'About the centre?' She nodded, and he gasped. 'So why does he think your father wrote to him?'

Catherine shrugged. 'I suppose he still thinks I was fooling around.'

'With other men?'

She nodded again. 'I expect so.'

Tony seethed. 'As if your father would have cared about that,' he muttered. 'The man's a fool!'

'Don't say that. That's what he said. Oh, it's all my own fault. I shouldn't have let him—think I was—well, I didn't know what was going to happen, did I?'

Tony shook his head. 'Couldn't you tell him?'

'Tell him? Tell him what?' Catherine suppressed the emotion inside her. 'I have nothing to say to Jared Royal! I—I despise him!'

'No, you don't.' Tony was resigned.

'I do. I despise him. I despise everything he stands for.'

Tony heaved a sigh. 'So?'

'All right, all right. I'll come back to London.' Now that the decision was made, she was eager to leave. 'When shall we go?'

Tony frowned. 'I'll have Manners take a trip to the airport this afternoon. With luck, we might get a flight tomorrow.'

'Tomorrow?' Catherine was shocked.

'Is that too soon?'

'Oh, no—no.' But it was. And the idea of leaving and never seeing Jared again filled her with despair.

She met Tony in the library before dinner. They had arranged to meet there a little earlier than usual so that they had time to speak together before Elizabeth—and perhaps Jared—appeared.

'Six o'clock tomorrow,' he said, without preamble. 'We get into Heathrow just after six. The following day, of course.'

'Of course.' Catherine understood the time change. 'Six o'clock. Was there nothing earlier in the day?'

Tony half smiled. 'Don't be so eager! Besides, it's the direct flight. I thought you'd prefer that.'

'Yes, I would.' Catherine moved restlessly, the skirt of the long amber-coloured caftan she was wearing swirling about her slender legs. 'I suppose—I suppose I'll have to tell Jared.'

'No need. I already did.'

'What?' She stared at him.

'I did. He was sitting on the verandah when Manners got back this afternoon, and when I wheeled the old chair out to meet my man, he was there. So I told him.'

Catherine felt sick. 'What did he say?'

Tony frowned. 'He didn't say much at all at first, so I also told him what I thought of him for disbelieving all the work you've put in towards the centre——'

'Oh, Tony!'

'Well, why not? I don't see why he should go on hugging that particular belief. I told him he could verify everything I said by contacting the committee in London, but I don't think he'll do that.'

'Tony, you should have left that alone.'

'Why? I wanted him to feel bad. Why should you suffer all the humiliation for nothing?'

'So—so what did he say then?'

Tony shrugged. 'Not a lot. Actually, he asked some pertinent questions about what we're trying to do, and asked how much money we needed.'

157

Catherine folded her arms across her body. Although it was a warm evening, she felt chilled. Her last evening in Barbados, she thought bleakly. She should be feeling relieved, not devastated.

'So that's settled,' added Tony comfortably. 'And I've assuaged my conscience. I couldn't leave here without telling Royal the truth.'

'Catherine!' She started, but it was only Elizabeth coming into the room behind her, holding out a hand. 'I've just heard the news! You're leaving us!'

Catherine turned to face the older woman reluctantly. She knew the triumph she would see in her eyes, and she was not disappointed. 'Did Jared tell you?' she asked tightly.

'Jared?' Elizabeth's eyes flickered. 'Is he here? I—no, he didn't tell me. It was Susie, actually. I understand you're leaving with Tony and Mr Manners. It was he who let it out to the servants. You ought to have told me,' she added reproachfully. 'I could have arranged a little going-away party.'

To replace the one Jared had cancelled, thought Catherine bitterly. Poor John had been most put out when she told him.

'I don't think Catherine would want anything like that,' put in Tony. 'But it was a kind thought. Is Jared joining us for dinner?'

'I don't know.' Elizabeth looked agitated for a moment. 'I haven't seen him today. I thought he was down at the beach house.'

'He was here earlier,' said Tony.

'I'm here now,' remarked Jared briefly, and Catherine glanced round as he walked into the room. 'Can I offer you all a drink?'

While he mixed their drinks, Elizabeth made small talk,

mentioning the flight back to London, asking Catherine how long it would take to get from the airport to her flat.

'I expect you're looking forward to seeing all your old friends,' she observed, still with a trace of malice. 'A girl like you must have lots of—friends.'

'Of course she does,' exclaimed Tony staunchly. 'And they're not all paraplegics either!'

Elizabeth's smile was forced. 'I can see you're very fond of her, Tony,' she told him coyly.

'I am,' he asserted, reaching for Catherine's hand. 'I'd marry her tomorrow, if I was a whole man.'

'Tony!'

Catherine was embarrassed, but he just squeezed her hand more tightly. 'What's the matter, old love? I'm only saying what's true. You know I've always been your slave.'

'Dinner is served, Mr Royal.'

Lily's announcement could not have come soon enough for Catherine, and releasing Tony's hand, she moved round to take charge of his chair. As she did so, she encountered Jared's eyes upon her, but she looked away from the cold penetration of his gaze.

The meal seemed endless, and Catherine longed to escape to her room and do her packing. Even Tony's company had no appeal this evening, and as soon as she reasonably could, she excused herself, and left the room. But footsteps followed hers, and in the hall, Jared's voice arrested her.

'Catherine! I want to speak to you.'

She turned reluctantly to face him. 'Oh? Why? You haven't had anything to say all week.'

His brow creased angrily. 'You don't imagine I'm going to let you leave, do you?' he demanded.

Catherine swallowed convulsively. 'What do you mean?'

'I think we should go into the library. We can talk privately there.'

'I don't want to go into the library,' she replied tremulously.

'Nevertheless, you will,' he told her, and when she would have resisted him, he took her arm and half dragged her after him along the corridor and in through the open double doors. Leaving her to rub her bruised skin, he closed the doors and then turned to face her. 'Now—I repeat: you are not leaving!'

Catherine was suddenly very calm. Tony was right. Jared could not force her to remain here. 'You can't stop me,' she said.

'Catherine, for God's sake——'

'I'm leaving, Jared. I should never have come here. You never really wanted me to. I've caused nothing but trouble. You should be glad to see me go.'

'Catherine!' He spoke through his teeth. 'All right, all right—perhaps I have been punishing you this week——'

'Punishing me?' She looked incredulously at him.

'Yes. Punishing you.' He ran a weary hand round the back of his neck, disordering his hair, the buttons of his shirt straining apart to reveal the hair-darkened skin of his chest. 'It may amuse you to know that I've punished myself, too.'

Catherine didn't want to listen to him. Her mind was made up. She was leaving tomorrow afternoon. Jared was going to marry Laura, and whatever he said, staying here could only prolong the eventual agony.

'You're wasting your time, Jared.' She was amazed at how cold her voice sounded even to her ears. 'Now, if that's all you have to say . . .'

'*Catherine!*' He caught her by the shoulders, his fingers digging into her flesh, his eyes grim with impatience. 'I don't think you understand.'

'It's you who doesn't understand, Jared.'

'Oh, I admit—when I first found out how you had tricked me, I was mad! Can you blame me? But it hasn't been easy, and after what Tony told me this afternoon ... Perhaps we were both at fault. Perhaps I misjudged you——'

'*Perhaps?*'

'—but I'm a jealous man! I never thought I could want any woman who had—who wasn't——' He broke off frustratedly. 'What I'm trying to say is, if I have to choose, I'd rather have you as you are than not at all!'

Catherine gasped. 'Shop-soiled? Is that what you mean?'

'Don't put labels on people, Catherine. God, I'm doing this badly——'

'Yes, you are.' She thrust him away from her, and stood panting in front of him. 'You—you—I hope I never have to see you again!'

'You don't mean that.'

'Don't I?'

His face was very pale, but she scarcely noticed it.

'I love you, Catherine.'

'Love?' She almost laughed in his face. 'You don't know the meaning of the word!'

And brushing past him, she left the room. She felt chilled, numb, completely without emotion. These weeks in Barbados had been an experience she was never likely to forget. An experience it would not *pay* her to forget ...

Laura came to lunch the following day.

Catherine had seen no sign of Jared since the scene they had had in the library the night before, and judging by Elizabeth's tight expression, she guessed he had made himself unavailable to her as well. But Laura was quite another matter.

'But this is so sudden, isn't it?' she exclaimed, looking

161

blankly from Catherine to Tony. 'You didn't mention you were leaving so soon, either of you.'

'Well, I have a job of work to do, old love,' remarked Tony, with his easy familiarity. 'I'm not like you lotus-eaters, you know. I have to earn my living.'

Laura made an impatient gesture. 'But Jared told me you were staying for at least six months, Catherine,' she protested.

Catherine bent her head. In Laura's position, she doubted she would have been complaining. She shook her head. Laura was too nice a girl, that was her trouble. She asked to be hurt. And Jared would hurt her, even in her numbed state Catherine understood that.

'I—I suppose, like Tony, I want to get back to work,' she said at last.

'Work?' Elizabeth entered the conversation for the first time. 'What work do you do, Catherine?'

'Quite a lot, actually,' interposed Tony swiftly, detecting the scathing note in Elizabeth's voice. 'Catherine drives. She has her own car. It's useful for our organisation to have members who are not handicapped in any way. Do you know, she raised funds through jumble sales and raffles, that sort of thing, to buy a specially equipped mini-bus to take our really handicapped members on outings?'

'Really?' Elizabeth was not impressed.

'That's wonderful!' Laura looked envious. 'I wish I could do something like that. One can get bored with socialising all the time.'

'Well, you'll be married soon,' put in Elizabeth silkily. 'Then you won't have time to feel bored. And once you start a family . . .'

'Yes.' But Laura did not sound so convinced. She continued to look wistfully at Catherine and Tony, and it was obvious that for once she was taking little notice of her stepmother-in-law to be.

Although she told herself that she was glad he had not put in an appearance, Catherine was surprised when Jared did not return before they left for the airport. Sylvester was driving them, and it was, amazingly, quite a wrench, even saying goodbye to Elizabeth and Laura, watching their figures grow smaller as the distance between them and the moving car lengthened.

At the airport they had to wait for some time after checking in, but Tony kept up a steady flow of conversation, and although Catherine knew why he was doing it, the therapy worked just the same.

It was when they were actually boarding the airliner that she thought she saw Jared, but she told herself she must have been imagining things. Nevertheless, there was something familiar about the man seated astride the motor-cycle at the edge of the runway, and who else but a Royal could have gained access anyway ...

CHAPTER ELEVEN

LONDON was still cold, doubly so, after the heat they had left behind, but spring was on its way. There were tulips and daffodils everywhere, and the trees in the parks were burgeoning with new life.

It was good to be back at the flat. It was good to be amongst things and people she knew again. And Catherine enjoyed the sensation of being her own mistress once more.

During the first few days she took things easy, getting back into the swing of things. Mrs Forrest, her daily, had kept the flat in good order, but it lacked those lived-in touches which Catherine took pleasure in replacing. She bought books and magazines, treated herself to some new cosmetics, and filled the rooms with spring flowers. But she refused to admit to the awareness that no matter how many blooms she bought, she could never emulate the perfumes and colours of Amaryllis.

She went to see her solicitors, and explained that she was now back in London again. They seemed surprised, but not unduly so, and she guessed they imagined she had come back because she had been bored.

Life took on a pattern. She picked up the old threads without too much difficulty, and found in her work with Tony the escape she needed from the tortuous workings of her subconscious. Asleep, she couldn't prevent the dreams from coming, and in consequence she invariably awoke feeling more exhausted than when she had gone to bed.

Tony's headquarters were situated on the ground floor of an old house he owned in Ealing. The top two floors and the basement were useless to people who spent their lives in wheelchairs, but they were rented out to an assortment of other organisations as committee rooms, offices, and the like, the income helping towards the association's funds. From here, Tony directed the whole operation, and although the paper was peeling off the walls and the woodwork had seen better days, there was so much warmth and enthusiasm expended here that Catherine had always liked to be part of it. She had got involved indirectly during her final year at school, when some of the older pupils had organised a working party to help the old and the handicapped, and once she had got to know Tony, she had never looked back. She shared his dream of a modern equipped centre, somewhere that combined practical working facilities with recreational ones.

During the following weeks Catherine tried to throw off her depression, spending long hours working at the centre, or out collecting articles for a charity auction she was planning. She fell into bed at night, too tired to think of anything but sleep, but the restlessness of those periods of unconsciousness left dark rings around her eyes. Tony was becoming quite worried about her, but she managed to waylay his suspicions by wearing a heavier make-up.

One morning she arrived at the centre to find the place in uproar. Jerry Allan, one of Tony's satellites, met her in the hall. He was a spastic, who had spent all his life in a wheelchair, but this morning he was fairly jumping out of his seat.

'Wait until you see Tony!' he exclaimed, grinning. 'Just you wait.'

Catherine stared at him in astonishment. 'Why? What is it? What's happened?'

Jerry shook his head. 'Well—no, I can't tell you. It wouldn't be fair. It's Tony's news. He'll tell you himself.'

'Tell me what?'

'Go on, go in. You'll find out.'

With an exasperated sigh, Catherine pushed open Tony's office door. The room was filled with people, and she looked over their heads at Tony at his desk. 'What's going on?' she exclaimed, half laughing. 'Has someone won the pools?'

'Better than that, Cat,' Tony called above the din of voices. 'We've had a donation. A donation towards the new centre. Wait for it—one hundred thousand pounds!'

Catherine grasped the door post to support herself. 'A hundred thousand pounds?' she echoed weakly. 'But—but who——?'

'We don't know.' Tony waved the cheque excitedly. 'An anonymous donor. But it's valid. I've already rung the bank, and they've verified that the cheque won't bounce.'

Catherine's legs felt terribly shaky, and she moved to sit on the side of his desk. 'But didn't the bank tell you?' she protested.

'Of course not. That's private information. It's all been done through solicitors. You know how these things are. But why worry? We've got it, and that's all we need to know. You realise what it means, of course. We can actually start looking for a site for the new centre!'

'Aren't you thrilled?' cried Barbara Collins, Tony's secretary, from behind her desk.

'I think the shock's been too much for her,' remarked David Johnson, one of the older members of the group, whose disabilities stemmed from injuries he had received during the war.

'You do look rather pale,' agreed Tony anxiously. 'What is it, old love? Aren't you feeling well?'

'I'm feeling fine,' Catherine protested hastily, but was she? It was wonderful news, of course. This money, together with the several thousands they already had in the

166

bank, would enable Tony to offer the contracts for the new centre, and her donation—the donation her father had been so opposed to—would no longer be quite so necessary.

And it was more than that. The new centre had never been quite real to her, it had been a goal to work for, but that was all. Now that it was within reach, her efforts would no longer need to be so urgent.

Tony cleared his office a few minutes later, and when they were alone, he said quietly: 'You don't have to pretend with me, Cat. I know what's wrong. You've been half killing yourself with work these past few weeks, and now you think the effort's been for nothing.'

'No!' She shook her head vigorously. 'Tony, I'm not selfish enough to want your hopes never to be fulfilled!'

'No,' he conceded. 'But you haven't fooled me, old love. Since you came back from Barbados, this place has been a kind of hair shirt for you. I don't know what it is you think you need to scourge yourself of, but sooner or later you had to start living with yourself again, without all this expension of energy.'

Catherine got up from the desk and walked across the room, looking out on the backs of a row of dingy houses behind. 'I just wanted to work, that was all,' she said tightly.

'No, that wasn't all,' Tony contradicted her dryly. 'You've been wearing yourself out. Why?'

'You're imagining things, Tony——'

'No, I'm not. I've wanted to say this for some time, Catherine. If you go on at this rate, you'll give yourself a nervous breakdown!' He sighed. 'It's Royal, isn't it? God, I should have known. I should never have suggested you came back.'

Catherine swung round. 'I—I would have done, anyway. I couldn't stay there.'

'Because Jared Royal was marrying Laura,' commented

167

Tony heavily. 'For no other reason.'

Catherine clenched her fists. 'You don't know that.'

'Then you tell me what's eating you up.'

'Nothing's eating me up! I—I've been sleeping badly, that's all.'

'And it has nothing to do with the fact that he should be a married man by now? That he and Laura are man and wife, living together, eating together—sleeping together?'

'Oh——' Catherine's composure snapped, and a sob caught in her throat. 'Th-that's a rotten thing to—to say!' she gulped, and turned away as the hot tears, which had been so long in coming, overran her eyes and flooded down her cheeks.

Tony let her cry for a few minutes, and then he came round the desk, propelling his wheelchair to her side, and putting his arm comfortingly around her waist.

'Don't you know it's better to cry?' he demanded huskily. 'Emotions build up inside you. If you don't let them out, they start to tear you to pieces.'

Catherine took the handkerchief he offered and rubbed her eyes. 'I'm so selfish!' she sobbed, into the square of white linen. 'You've had such good news, and I'm spoiling it all for you.'

'Nonsense!' Tony was brisk. 'That's what—friends are for. And I can never be anything more than a friend,' he finished gruffly, 'so don't deny me that, at least.'

'Oh, Tony,' she whispered, looking down at him tremulously. 'I love Jared.'

'I know you do,' he said, without rancour. 'But we both know that's no good, don't we?' She nodded mutely, and he made a determined gesture. 'So—you have to live with it, and—*we* have work to do.'

Surprisingly, there seemed more work to do in the next couple of weeks than less. The architects had to be con-

168

tacted, and their original plans studied and in some cases modified, the local council played their part in finding a suitable building site, and there were letters to be written to builders and contractors, as well as the normal day-to-day running of the Ealing centre.

Catherine threw herself wholeheartedly into the scheme, sometimes working late into the evening, discussing the recreational priorities with Tony, deciding what should come first in the initial stages of the building.

They had been working one evening and were about to go out in search of a drink and supper, when the doorbell rang. Leaving Tony to tidy up his desk, Catherine went to answer it, stepping back aghast when she opened the door and the light from the hall behind her illuminated the face of the girl waiting outside.

'Laura!' she exclaimed, in amazement. 'Good heavens, what are you doing here?'

Automatically, her eyes went beyond the girl, but there was no one with her, and reaction sent a shudder of apprehension over her body.

'Hey, Catherine.' Laura took an involuntary step forward. 'Gosh, you don't look at all well. I'm sorry if I've shocked you, but I've been hanging about your flat for ages, and then a neighbour told me you could usually be found down here. I thought I'd come and find you. Can I come in? Is this the famous centre?'

Catherine stepped aside, shaking her head, and Tony, who had emerged from his office to see what was going on, exclaimed: 'Hardly famous, Laura, but it will be!' He grinned, propelling his chair forward. 'This is a pleasant surprise. I didn't know you were spending your honeymoon in London.'

Catherine closed the door, and leaned weakly back against it. Trust Tony to come straight to the point, she

169

thought bitterly. But perhaps it was the best way. There was no point in trying to avoid the facts.

'I'm not.' Laura's reply was a shock. She extended her hand for them to see. 'I'm not even engaged, let alone married! The wedding's off, as they say.'

She spoke lightly, with only an underlying note of regret in her voice. Tony exchanged a glance with Catherine, saw how pale she had become, and indicated his office behind him.

'Come along in for a minute. We—Cat and I—we were just going out for supper, but we can talk more comfortably here.' He waited until both girls were seated, and then he added: 'So what are you doing in London?'

Laura shrugged. Then she looked at Catherine, and a faintly compassionate look crossed her face. 'I could say I came to find you,' she said, with a sigh. 'But that wouldn't be true.' She bit her lip. 'You haven't seen Jared, have you?'

'Seen Jared?' Catherine almost choked on the words. 'How—I mean—how could I have seen Jared?'

'Because he's here—in London,' replied Laura simply. 'He's been here about two months.'

'Two months?' Catherine realised she was repeating everything Laura said parrot-fashion, but she couldn't help herself.

Tony took over the questioning. 'Why would Jared come to London?' he exclaimed.

Laura hunched her shoulders, rubbing her bare finger almost unknowingly. 'Who knows? He says he wants to paint here. But as far as I can see, he's done nothing so far.'

'You've seen him?'

Catherine couldn't prevent the involuntary words, and Laura nodded. 'Today. This afternoon. That's really why I came to England. Elizabeth's been so worried about him. He hasn't written, he hasn't phoned. He hasn't contacted her at all. She only found his address because for some reason he had given it to his solicitors.'

'And—the engagement's off?' Tony prompted.

'Oh, yes. That was off a couple of weeks before he left Barbados. Just after you left actually, Catherine. I'm sure you know why.'

Catherine couldn't take all this in. She felt sick with reaction, filled with an incredulous anticipation that weakened her knees and turned her stomach into a churning cauldron.

'I—are you saying Jared broke his engagement to you because—because of me?' she whispered disbelievingly, and Laura sighed.

'Don't sound so surprised. Jared's engagement to me never meant a lot. I realise now he only did it to silence the gossips after his father died, and he and Elizabeth were alone at the house. After you arrived—well, you know what happened as well as I do.'

'But—but——' Catherine couldn't find words to say what she wanted to say. 'Wh-why didn't he tell me?'

'I thought he did.' Laura frowned. 'I understand you turned him down.'

'I—turned—him—down?' Catherine's mouth was dry. 'But he never mentioned—marriage to me!'

'Well, what did you think he meant?' Laura sounded impatient now. 'Surely you know Jared well enough to know he would never countenance anything else? Good lord, surely you realise he only brought Tony out to Barbados to find out if you cared about him.'

'Cared about who? Jared? Or Tony?'

'Why, Tony, of course. I think he thought you and he had been having some big scene. He wanted to see for himself.'

'Oh, no!'

Catherine got up out of her chair to pace disbelievingly

171

across the room. Of course, Laura didn't know about that business of the pregnancy! It was suddenly clear what Jared had wanted to do. He had thought she was expecting Tony's child. He had wanted to see for himself what kind of relationship they had. Would he have married her in spite of the child if he had been satisfied they no longer cared for one another? Oh, God, it all made a crazy kind of sense. And she had turned him away because he had shown that she had hurt him ...

She turned to Laura. 'Where is he?'

Laura's eyes widened. 'Jared?' She hesitated. 'I'm not sure I should tell you.'

'Why not?'

Laura shrugged. 'I don't think you'd want to see him. He's changed. So coarse and unkempt. If you could turn him down at Amaryllis, you will certainly turn him down now.'

'Where is he?' Catherine persisted, and Tony said quietly: 'You'd better tell her, Laura.'

Laura hesitated a moment longer, and then opening her handbag, she took out a slip of paper. 'This is his address. But I warn you, he may not want to see you. He wouldn't let me in, and I've flown more than three thousand miles!'

Catherine turned the paper over. 'Coniston Street?' she said blankly. 'Where's that?'

Tony was frowning. 'Isn't it in Chelsea?'

'I don't know.' Laura was indifferent. 'I just asked a cab driver, and he took me there. I think he mentioned— King's Road.'

'That's Chelsea,' said Tony definitely. 'I thought I knew it. It's not far from the football ground, Cat.'

'I'll find it.' Catherine was already pulling on the fringed cream suede jacket that matched the calf-length dress she was wearing. She paused at the door. 'Oh—and thank you, Laura.'

Laura moved her shoulders dismissingly. 'Don't thank me yet. You may find it's a wasted journey . . .'

But Catherine had gone, the door banging noisily behind her.

It wasn't easy finding an unknown destination by the light of street lamps. A policeman gave her directions, but even then she almost missed the turning, and heard someone blare their car horn noisily at her.

Coniston Street was a row of old Victorian houses which had seen better days, presently converted into flats and bed-sitters. The number on the slip of paper Laura had given her was forty-seven, and it was about half way down the street on the left-hand side. Catherine managed to squeeze her Mini into the space between an old Vauxhall and a transit wagon, impatience making the exercise twice as long as it should have taken.

She climbed the steps up to the door and saw the list of tenants with their individual bell pushes. Two names too complicated to pronounce, a Philips, a Kenilworth, and a Brown. And that was all. She examined them again, a little desperately this time. Ahmed Mahdu . . . She gave up the rest. That definitely wasn't Jared. Viktor Czyviarchos. She shook her head. M. Philips. Maurice Kenilworth. J. Brown. She backtracked. *J*. Brown. She fumbled in her bag and brought out the slip of paper again. The number was definitely forty-seven. It had to be worth a try. If only Laura had explained! But who could blame her for being a little obstructive?

She pressed the button beside J. Brown, and waited. Nothing happened. She pressed it again. And again nothing happened. She sighed, and stepped back down a couple of steps to look up at the windows of the house. There were lights in several of them.

Going back up the steps again, she pressed J. Brown's button once more, and when still it was ignored, she pressed the button beside M. Philips. Whether Mr Philips, or *Miss* Philips, was expecting visitors, she never did find out, but at that moment the door released itself, and swung invitingly inwards.

She took a step forward, and then gulped as a group of Indians confronted her in the hall. But they smiled politely, and on impulse, she asked if they knew where she could find Mr Brown.

'The top floor,' one of them told her immediately, gesturing her towards the stairs. 'Two flights up.'

'Thank you,' she smiled. But she waited until they had closed the outer door behind them before starting the long climb.

She was breathless by the time she reached the second floor, and she stood for a moment regaining her breath before deciding which of the two doors to choose. Then, running a smoothing hand over her hair, she knocked determinedly at the one to her left.

She had half expected to have to stand there knocking for ages before he answered, but to her surprise, the door opened almost immediately, and an angry voice exclaimed: 'For God's sake, Laura——' before breaking off abruptly as he saw her. He stared at her disbelievingly for a long disturbing minute, and then she said quietly: 'Can I come in?'

She had been shocked by his appearance, she couldn't deny it, and when he stood reluctantly aside to let her enter the flat, her legs moved almost automatically. He was so thin, he was almost emaciated, and his hair was shoulder-length, matching the growth of beard on his chin. She would never have recognised him as the arrogant owner of Amaryllis, or indeed as Jared Royal, portrait painter and landscape artist. And yet he looked more like everyone's idea of an artist now than any other time in his life. If he had wanted to disguise himself, he could not have done it more successfully. But at what cost?

The flat was small and untidy, and it stank of stale liquor and cigarettes. Low windows were set in walls that sloped down with the eaves of the house, and through their open panes came the low rumble of the city traffic. Catherine gave one comprehensive look around her, and then she exclaimed frustratedly: 'Oh, Jared! You could afford better than this!'

He had closed the door and seemed to be getting over the shock of finding her outside. 'This is good enough for me,' he told her harshly. 'You must excuse the mess. I never was much good at housework.'

Catherine drew a trembling breath. 'What are you doing in London, Jared? You told me you disliked the place.'

Jared shrugged. 'I thought it was time I expanded my field.'

'But'—Catherine looked about her. 'Where's your painting equipment? Have you done any work since you came here?'

Jared held up his head, surveying her with a little of his earlier arrogance. 'I don't think you have the right to ask a question like that,' he said.

Catherine twisted the strap of her handbag. 'I don't, of course. But—but finding you like this ...'

'How did you find me? Laura, I suppose.'

Catherine nodded. 'She came—she came to the centre.'

'You're still working there, then?' He spoke heavily.

'Of course. Why shouldn't I be?'

He shook his head. 'Why have you come here, Catherine?'

Catherine made a helpless little gesture. 'To see you, of course.'

'Why?' His lips twisted. 'Did Laura tell you what a squalid little place I had? Did you want to see it for yourself?'

'*No!*' Catherine drew an unsteady breath. 'Jared, you have to tell me—why did you break your engagement to Laura?'

He walked slowly across the room to where a bottle of Scotch resided on a low table. He held up the bottle to show Catherine, but she shook her head, watching him as he bent and poured some for himself into a thick glass. He was wearing jeans, and as he bent to his task, his denim shirt parted from the waistband of his pants, revealing bony hips. It was the last straw as far as Catherine was concerned. With a little sob, she dropped her bag on the floor, and covered the space between them, winding her arms around his waist from behind, pressing her face against the rough, sweaty material of his shirt.

'Jared, Jared!' she breathed, tears dampening her cheeks, wetting his shirt. 'Oh, Jared—I love you!'

He had stiffened as she touched him, the untasted glass of whisky halfway to his lips. He remained motionless for fully half a minute, and then he carefully lowered the glass on to the tray, and turning, put his hands on her shoulders, propelling her away from him.

'Now hear this!' he muttered roughly. 'I don't need your pity, Catherine!'

'Pity?' She stared up into his face. 'Jared, if I pity you, I pity myself as well. For—for all the time we've wasted.'

He thrust her away from him, tugging impatiently at the hair at the back of his neck, but his hands were shaking. 'What has Laura been telling you?' he demanded. 'Why have you come here now? Why now?'

Catherine spread her hands. 'I couldn't come sooner. I didn't know you were here.'

'And you didn't trouble to find out, did you?' he muttered bitterly.

'To find out?' She was confused. 'How could I have found out? I've had no contact with you since I left.'

'But Liz wrote you. She told you the wedding was off.'

'Elizabeth—wrote to me?' Catherine blinked rapidly. 'When? When did she write to me?'

Jared shook his head. 'I don't know exactly. After I told her it was all over between me and Laura.'

'But I got no letter!'

His eyes narrowed. 'You must have done.'

'I didn't, I tell you!' She made a futile gesture. 'Oh, what's the use, you won't believe me, will you?'

Jared took a step towards her. 'I asked Liz to write to you,' he said. 'I—God help me, I didn't know what to say —what I *could* say after—after——'

Catherine caught her breath. 'Did you—did you actually see the letter?'

Jared frowned distractedly. 'I don't know. No, no, I don't believe I did.' He closed his eyes. 'She didn't write, is that what you're saying?'

'If you believe me.'

His eyes opened again, staring into hers, bloodshot, but no less penetrating. 'I have to believe you,' he muttered. 'For my own sanity.' He took another step towards her. 'So you didn't know that—that Laura and I . . .'

'No. I thought you were—married.'

'And Laura told you otherwise.'

'Tonight,' Catherine nodded.

'And—that made the difference? Nothing else?'

'What else could there be?' she cried.

He hesitated a moment, and then he nodded. 'Indeed.

177

What else?'

'Oh, Jared, I've been through hell!'

'Not the hell I've been through,' he groaned, and unable to prevent himself, he pulled her into his arms, shuddering down the length of his body as his hands slid possessively over hers. He buried his face in her neck, his beard rough against her soft skin, just holding her close against him until she felt the hardening pressure of his thighs. 'God— oh, God, I want you, Catherine.'

Then, when she expected him to kiss her, he drew away from her again, trembling as he raked unsteady hands through his hair.

'This is no good,' he said thickly. 'I'm not fit to touch you. I haven't had a bath in days, and I don't remember the last time I ate. I think it was yesterday—or maybe the day before.'

'Jared!'

She caught his arm, but he released himself shakily, and she realised he was half fainting with weakness.

'Let me get a wash and a change of clothes,' he told her unevenly. 'Then I'll be fine.'

'You won't be fine!' she protested, half tearfully, although she knew tears were no good right now. 'You haven't been looking after yourself at all, have you? Dear God, Jared, do you realise, another two months of this and you'd be dead!'

He sought the back of an armchair for support, forcing a smile. 'I—had nothing to live for, did I?' he asked, with an attempt at lightness, and Catherine felt a surge of primitive hatred for Elizabeth for allowing this to happen.

She must have known how he felt, why he came to London. Yet she had been prepared to let him go on thinking the worst, that Catherine didn't care about him. If she hadn't become concerned because he had not contacted her and sent Laura to find him ...

And of course, the last person she would expect Laura to contact would be Catherine. She had obviously overlooked Laura's gentler character, and her interest in Tony's rehabilitation centre. Had this been Elizabeth's way of paying them both back for what she thought were her grievances? But even she could have had no idea of the real state of Jared's health.

'Where is the bathroom?' Catherine asked now, and Jared nodded towards the kitchen. 'Through there.'

Ignoring the urge to take him in her arms, she brushed past him and switched on the light in the kitchenette. It was small and rather grubby, but a rapid exploration revealed that the bath folded away beneath the sink, and it was large and reasonably clean. She would have liked to have taken him to her own flat with its more modern conveniences, but she guessed he did not have enough strength to trail down all those stairs and up others. This would have to do, and turning on the taps at the sink, she began to fill the dish preparatory to transferring its contents to the bath.

Jared came to the door, leaning against the jamb for support. 'What are you doing?'

'I'm filling you a bath.'

'I can do that.'

'No, you can't.' She resisted his attempt to grasp her wrist. 'You see—you haven't the strength.' She bit back another wave of anxiety, and indicated his shirt and jeans. 'You'd better start undressing.'

A look of self-contempt crossed his face. 'I won't let you bathe me.'

'I wasn't about to offer,' she retorted, pouring another dish of water into the bath. 'Hurry up. This won't take long. Then I'm going to prepare you some food.'

'I'm not hungry.'

'Nevertheless, you're going to eat something.'

'You're giving me orders?'

Catherine flushed. 'Yes.'

He shrugged and obediently started to unzip his pants. It was intoxicating having him at her mercy like this, but she guessed that it wouldn't last long. Once he had recovered his strength ... But then she wouldn't have it any other way.

She turned her back as he got into the bath, and then handing him the soap, she said: 'Where are your clean clothes?'

He sighed, relaxing lazily in the water, disturbingly sensual in this intimate state. 'I guess they're in the dressing table drawers,' he answered, looking up at her, and a quickening of emotion in his eyes made her catch her breath. 'Come here.'

She shook her head, albeit a little reluctantly. 'Not—not now.' She walked towards the door. 'You can give me a shout when you're finished.'

His bedroom was a small, single-bedded room opening off the living room, and these three rooms formed the flat. Going in there, Catherine grimaced at the tumbled bed and wrinkled sheets, stripping off the covers and rolling the linen up for washing. She found clean sheets in a chest of drawers, and remade the bed, finding pleasure in the task.

His clothes were in disorder in the drawers, and she pulled out a tangle of shirts and socks, dislodging some papers as she did so.

They fluttered to the floor, and as she bent to pick them up, she saw that one was a copy draft on a London bank for a sum of money which not long ago had figured so prominently in every conversation at the centre. *One hundred thousand pounds*! It could not be a coincidence. And

180

she sank down weakly on to the side of the bed, staring at the draft disbelievingly.

She ought to have guessed, she supposed, although it was such a large sum of money, she could see no reason why he should have donated it. And yet he had. It was there in black and white. And the other papers only verified what she suspected.

She looked across the living room to the kitchen door. Perhaps that was what he had meant when he had asked her why she had come here. Perhaps he had been afraid Laura had revealed the truth of what he had done.

She was still sitting there when she heard him getting out of the bath, and she pushed the papers away again, knowing she could not mention them now. She had not found his underclothes, but she had found a navy bathrobe, so she walked back to the kitchen with that.

Jared was standing at the sink when she re-entered the kitchen, the towel tucked around his hips, using his razor. He had washed his hair and it was damp and tousled; the beard had disappeared. Already he looked years younger, if no less gaunt. He rinsed the lather from his jaw and turned to face her.

'I——' Catherine's mouth was unaccountably dry—'I couldn't find your underclothes, so I brought this.' She held out the bathrobe.

'Thanks.'

He came to take the robe. Even barefoot, he was taller than she was in her heels, steadier now than before his bath. He unhitched the towel and let it fall to the floor, and then, with a muffled exclamation, he gathered her into his arms, finding her mouth with his, parting her lips with his tongue and kissing her with hungry urgency.

'Mmm, Catherine, you smell so good!' he groaned, his fingers finding the long zip at the back of her dress and

181

steadily impelling it downwards.

'You—must be hungry,' she got out breathlessly, but he only gathered her closer, letting her feel the effect she had on him.

'Only for you,' he breathed into her ear. 'Only for you.' Then he swung her up into his arms, ignoring her protest, carrying her rather unsteadily across the living room and into his bedroom, laying her on his bed almost reverently. 'Don't stop me, Catherine,' he implored, and she wound her arms round his neck, pulling him down to her.

'I wasn't going to,' she confessed helplessly.

Some time later, Jared rubbed his face against her bare shoulder, his hand cupping her throat possessively. 'Oh, Catherine!' he muttered huskily. 'I've been so wrong about you.'

'Do you mind?' she whispered, turning her head on the pillow to look at him.

'Mind?' He gave a rueful laugh. 'My darling, no one could love you more than I do. And it's me who should be asking you that question,' he added ungrammatically.

'Do I mind?' she murmured, stretching her arms luxuriously above her head. 'Hmm—I don't mind at all.'

Jared said a word that sent shivers of delight down her spine, and then caressing her mouth with his own, he said: 'I couldn't let you go. Not even when I knew——' He broke off with an endearing grimace. 'Oh, what the hell! We're getting married just as soon as I can get a licence, and something tells me I'm not going to be able to let you go until a piece of paper tells us it's legal.'

Catherine wound her arms round his neck. 'I wouldn't want to leave you,' she breathed, running her fingers through his hair. 'Oh, Jared, I do love you.'

His eyes darkened passionately. 'You know what you're

inviting, don't you?'

She smiled complacently. 'You've just shown me,' she said teasingly. Then: 'I ought to ring Tony. Just to let him know everything's all right.'

Jared looked down at her possessively. 'Tony,' he muttered. 'If you knew how I grew to hate that name!'

Catherine touched his mouth with her fingers. 'Poor Tony!'

'Poor Tony nothing. He caused me a hell of a lot of sleepless nights.' He paused. 'I could have killed you that day at the airport. I'd been building myself up to ask you to marry me in spite of—well, you know in spite of what. When I saw Tony, I didn't know what to believe.'

Catherine hesitated. 'Would you—I mean, did you really want to marry me, believing I was—pregnant?'

Jared buried his face in the hollow between her breasts. 'I knew I'd never marry anyone else,' he replied softly.

'Oh, darling!'

Jared lifted his head. 'So many things conspired against us. I'm not blaming you. I resented the effect you had on me right from the start. I guess that was why it was easier to be uncivil to you. To keep you at a distance.'

'And there was Laura,' she reminded him.

'Yes, Laura.' He rolled on to his back, and she propped herself up on one elbow looking down at him. 'We should never have got engaged. But Liz convinced me it was a good idea.' He looked squarely at her. 'Whatever you've been led to believe, there was never anything between Liz and me. She was my father's wife, and I respected her for that. I never saw her as anything else.'

'But—but that night we were on the beach. She said you had spoken to her then about the wedding. Was it—was it when you got back?'

'Honey, I didn't get back until after seven. After you

183

rode off and left me, I was pretty mad.' He reached up and pulled a strand of her hair. 'I must think of some punishment for that.' Then he went on: 'I stayed on the beach until after the sun was up. Then I walked back. She spoke to me when I was loading up the car.'

'About the wedding?'

'Catherine, I was still trying to convince myself that you meant nothing to me. But I couldn't do it at the house. I didn't trust myself not to—well, I had to get away. You know how successful that was. I came back and found you and—Laura found us.'

'You were so horrible to Laura that day.'

'I know, I know. But God help me, Catherine, they were tying me up, she and Liz. I knew what Liz was doing. I could see that she didn't like you, and she was afraid I might marry you instead of Laura if she didn't set the wheels in motion. But I couldn't go through with it. Seeing you—being with you—I was jealous of any man who came near you, including that playboy Dexter.'

'And yet you let me go.'

'I couldn't hold you there by force, and after that scene in the library, I thought you'd never forgive me. I did go to the airport, though. I saw you get on the plane.'

'So it was you!' Catherine's lips parted.

'Oh, yes, I was always around.' He gave a rueful sigh. 'The night you arrived at Amaryllis, I put you to bed. You didn't know that, did you? Susie had closed the shutters and removed the flowers, but I had to assure myself that you were all right. I think that was when I began to resent the power you had over me.'

Catherine hesitated. Then she said gently: 'Why did you donate that money to the centre, Jared?'

His brows drew together and he scowled. 'How do you know about that?' he demanded.

She sighed. 'When I was looking for your clean clothes, I found some papers. I didn't deliberately set out to read them, but I saw the bank draft and ...'

Her voice trailed away and she looked at him anxiously, half afraid he was going to be furious with her. But he had relaxed again.

'I suppose I would have had to tell you sooner or later,' he conceded dryly. 'As my wife, you'll have to access to all my financial affairs.' He gave a wry smile. 'It wasn't the unselfish act it appeared. I thought perhaps—if they had enough money to build the centre, you might get bored with the project and consider returning to Barbados.'

'Oh, Jared!' She bent her head and kissed his chest. 'That's all I ever wanted to do.'

For a few moments there was silence in the apartment, and then Jared rolled over, imprisoning her body beneath the weight of his.

'And now,' he said, with lazy mockery, 'I'm hungry. Did I hear you say something earlier about preparing me some food?'

Six weeks later, Catherine and Jared walked barefoot along the beach at Flintlock, their arms round each other's waists. It was twilight, and the sun was sinking in a glory of gold into the ocean.

'We ought to be getting back,' murmured Catherine reluctantly, and Jared pressed her closer. Five weeks of marriage had obviously agreed with him, and there was flesh on his bones again, as well as a lazy indolence in his walk.

Tonight there was to be a dinner party at Amaryllis, their first big dinner party since their return, and the guests of honour were to be the governor-general and his lady. Jared had finished the commission at long last, and tonight

185

he was presenting it.

'Come on,' he said now, turning away from the ocean and up towards the beach house. 'I've got something to show to you.'

Catherine waited until Jared had entered the building and lighted some candles before following him inside.

'Isn't the lamp working?' she asked, indicating the flickering light of the candles.

Jared grinned. 'Don't be so practical! Candlelight is more romantic.'

Catherine laughed. 'Darling, our guests will be at the house in less than an hour, and now that Elizabeth's got a home of her own and isn't there to greet them for us ... We don't have time to be romantic!'

'We always have time to be romantic,' her husband contradicted her, carrying a sheet-shrouded canvas into the light. 'Now—what do you think of this?'

He pulled the sheet away and Catherine gazed in awe at the painting confronting her. It was the ocean, wild and untrammelled, surf rising, white and spumed with foam. But the ocean was only the background. She stood in the foreground, slim and more beautiful than she knew herself to be, veils of green chiffon flowing round her, her hair as free and unbound as the ocean.

She raised bemused eyes to his face, and he pointed to the bottom of the painting. 'See,' he said. 'It has a title.'

Catherine saw. 'Wild Enchantress!' she read. 'But——'

'You—or the ocean?' he asked gently, and she nodded. 'Both, I guess. My past—and my future. Now do you understand why it took so long to finish the commission?'

'But you destroyed the sketches,' she protested.

Jared pulled her into his arms, his hands possessive upon her. 'Do you honestly think I need any sketches to remember every inch of you?' he demanded huskily, and

186

she pressed herself closer to him. 'About our guests,' he added softly, but she just burrowed closer.

'What was that you said about always having time for romance?' she whispered, and he chuckled as he kicked the door shut with his foot ...

Other titles available by Anne Mather in the Mills & Boon Romance series

For details of how to obtain the titles listed above, please turn to page 191.

If you want.....

MEMORABLE ROMANTIC NOVELS by GREAT AUTHORS at UNBEATABLE VALUE then Mills & Boon Classics are for you. 4 specially chosen reissues every month of the best in Romantic Fiction from our back list.

January's titles are:

BLUE JASMINE *by Violet Winspear*
A friend warned Lorna of the dangers in travelling alone to the Oasis of Fadna, but Lorna scoffed that she couldn't be alarmed by tales of ardent and dangerous Arabs who carry off lovely girls to their harems – 'The bedouin prefer their own kind of women.' But she was wrong!

THE VENGEFUL HEART *by Roberta Leigh*
Nigel Farnham was attractive, rich and successful – but Julia Trafford had not married him for any of these reasons. She had a darker and more complicated motive – one that was going to rebound on her . . .

WINTERSBRIDE *by Sara Seale*
Adam Chantry didn't want a wife, but he needed a mistress for his home and a companion for his child; so he married the waiflike Miranda, who needed a home and protection. But could any normal man or woman keep to such a dispassionate bargain without breaking the rules?

THE MARRIAGE OF CAROLINE LINDSAY
by Margaret Rome
Caroline had married Domenico Vicari to give a fatherless baby a home and security, on condition that the marriage remained one in name only. But what would Domenico's reaction be when he discovered that she had been deceiving him from the start?

BUY THEM TODAY only 40p

Forthcoming Paperbacks

ISLE AT THE RAINBOW'S END *by Anne Hampson*
For Kara there could be no romance on the island of Bali –
or could there?

THIS MAN HER ENEMY *by Lilian Peake*
Doranne hated Keiran Richmond, but he still had power
over her ...

SWEET PROMISE *by Janet Dailey*
Rafael Torres could wreck Erica's life – how was she to stop
him?

A SENSE OF WORDS *by Madeline Charlton*
Dieter disapproved of Judith – but she'd soon show him he
was wrong!

THE MARQUIS TAKES A WIFE *by Rachel Lindsay*
A visit to Africa involved Beth with the Marquis of Powys,
but she was only his grandmother's companion ...

BLUE SKIES, DARK WATERS *by Margaret Pargeter*
Jan was suspicious of Earl Elton, but then he seemed to
suspect *her* motives. And when she fell in love with him ...

THE MAN ON HALF-MOON *by Margaret Way*
Katharine's missing brother was her only problem, until she
met Curt Dangerfield!

THE BLACK KNIGHT *by Flora Kidd*
Sandy thought that Lymond Caldwell was like a knight of
olden days – but could he save her from falling in love?

THE UNWILLING BRIDEGROOM *by Roberta Leigh*
Melisande blackmailed André into marrying her – and only
then fell in love with him ...

TULIPS FOR AUGUSTA *by Betty Neels*
Until she found out how Susan fitted into Constantijn's
scheme of things, how could Augusta take him seriously?

35p net each

Available February 1977

Your Mills & Boon Selection

- [ ] 001
  THE BLACK CAMERON
  Jean S. MacLeod
- [ ] 006
  GREENFINGERS FARM
  Joyce Dingwell
- [ ] 132
  RIVER NURSE
  Joyce Dingwell
- [ ] 201
  THE WOLF OF HEIMRA
  Jean S. MacLeod
- [ ] 253
  MISS MIRANDA'S WALK
  Betty Beaty
- [ ] 288
  WINTERSBRIDE
  Sara Seale
- [ ] 304 MASTER
  OF NORMANHURST
  Margaret Malcolm
- [ ] 333
  REVOLT—AND VIRGINIA
  Essie Summers
- [ ] 783
  THE TREES OF TARRENTALL
  Linden Grierson
- [ ] 925
  PRIDE AND POWER
  Anne Hampson
- [ ] 926
  THE AMETHYST MEADOWS
  Iris Danbury
- [ ] 939
  FALCON ON THE MOUNTAIN
  Gwyn Lavender
- [ ] 949
  SWEET SUNDOWN
  Margaret Way
- [ ] 956
  LOVE AND LUCY BROWN
  Joyce Dingwell

- [ ] 961
  THAT SUMMER OF SURRENDER
  Rebecca Caine
- [ ] 966
  FOOD FOR LOVE
  Rachel Lindsay
- [ ] 971
  SEPTEMBER IN PARIS
  Andrea Blake
- [ ] 976
  DARK VIKING
  Mary Wibberley
- [ ] 981
  UNTIL WE MET
  Anne Weale
- [ ] 987
  A PAVEMENT OF PEARL
  Iris Danbury
- [ ] 992
  LOVE IN DISGUISE
  Rachel Lindsay
- [ ] 997
  THE KISSING GATE
  Joyce Dingwell
- [ ] 1002
  TEMPESTUOUS APRIL
  Betty Neels
- [ ] 1007
  COUNTRY OF THE VINE
  Mary Wibberley
- [ ] 1012
  QUICKSILVER SUMMER
  Dorothy Cork
- [ ] 1014
  ALL THE LONG SUMMER
  Lucy Gillen
- [ ] 1024
  STORM FLOWER
  Margaret Way
- [ ] 1035
  THE FIRE AND THE FURY
  Rebecca Stratton

All priced at 25p. Please tick your selection and use the handy
order form supplied overleaf.